THE GLENCOE LITERATURE LIBRARY

Hamlet

and Related Readings

Glencoe
McGraw-Hill

New York, New York   Columbus, Ohio   Woodland Hills, California   Peoria, Illinois

Acknowledgments

Grateful acknowledgment is given authors, publishers, photographers, museums, and agents for permission to reprint the following copyrighted material. Every effort has been made to determine copyright owners. In case of any omissions, the Publisher will be pleased to make suitable acknowledgments in future editions.

HAMLET by William Shakespeare. Edited by Cyrus Hoy. Copyright © 1992, 1963 by W. W. Norton & Company, Inc. All rights reserved. Published by arrangement with W. W. Norton & Company, Inc.

"The Management of Grief" from THE MIDDLEMAN AND OTHER STORIES by Bharati Mukherjee. Copyright © 1988 by Bharati Mukherjee. Used by permission of Grove/Atlantic, Inc.

"The Management of Grief" from THE MIDDLEMAN AND OTHER STORIES by Bharati Mukherjee. Copyright © 1988 by Bharati Mukherjee. Reprinted by permission of Penguin Books Canada Limited.

"The Embassy of Death: An Essay on *Hamlet*" reprinted from THE WHEEL OF FIRE by G. Wilson Knight, copyright © 1949 Methuen & Co., Ltd. Reprinted by permission of Routledge.

Excerpt from ROSENCRANTZ AND GUILDENSTERN ARE DEAD by Tom Stoppard. Copyright © 1967 by Tom Stoppard. Used by permission of Grove/Atlantic, Inc. and Faber & Faber Ltd.

"The Elizabethan Approach" from SHAKESPEARE AND HIS PLAYERS by Martin Holmes. Copyright © 1972 Martin Holmes. Reprinted by permission of John Murray Publishers, Ltd.

"Hamlet Soliloquy—Prince Charles," from THE FRIENDLY SHAKESPEARE by Norrie Epstein. Copyright © 1993 by Norrie Epstein, Jon Winokur, and Reid Boates. Used by permission of Viking Penguin, a division of Penguin Putnam Inc.

"The Character of Hamlet's Mother" by Carolyn Heilbrun reprinted by permission of SHAKESPEARE QUARTERLY.

Cover Art: *Hamlet and Horatio in the Cemetery*, 1839, Eugène Delacroix, Musée du Louvre, Paris/SuperStock.

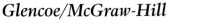

Glencoe/McGraw-Hill

A Division of The McGraw·Hill Companies

Send all inquiries to:
Glencoe/McGraw-Hill
8787 Orion Place
Columbus, OH 43240

ISBN 0-02-817986-2
Printed in the United States of America
2 3 4 5 6 7 8 9 026 04 03 02 01 00

Contents

Hamlet

Related Readings

Continued

Contents *Continued*

Hamlet

William Shakespeare

Characters

CLAUDIUS: King of Denmark

HAMLET: son to the former and nephew to the present King

POLONIUS: Lord Chamberlain

HORATIO: friend to Hamlet

LAERTES: son to Polonius

VOLTEMAND

CORNELIUS

ROSENCRANTZ

GUILDENSTERN } courtiers

OSRIC

A GENTLEMAN

A PRIEST

MARCELLUS

BERNARDO } officers

FRANCISCO: a soldier

REYNALDO: servant to Polonius

PLAYERS

TWO CLOWNS: grave-diggers

FORTINBRAS: Prince of Norway

A NORWEGIAN CAPTAIN

ENGLISH AMBASSADORS

GERTRUDE: Queen of Denmark and mother of Hamlet

OPHELIA: daughter to Polonius

GHOST OF HAMLET'S FATHER

LORDS, LADIES, OFFICERS, SOLDIERS, SAILORS, MESSENGERS, ATTENDANTS

SETTING: Denmark

Act 1

Scene 1

[*Enter* BERNARDO *and* FRANCISCO, *two sentinels.*]

    BER. Who's there?

    FRAN. Nay, answer me. Stand and unfold yourself.

    BER. Long live the king!

    FRAN. Bernardo?

5   **BER.** He.

    FRAN. You come most carefully upon your hour.

    BER. 'Tis now struck twelve. Get thee to bed, Francisco.

    FRAN. For this relief much thanks. 'Tis bitter cold,
    And I am sick at heart.

10   **BER.** Have you had quiet guard?

    FRAN.   Not a mouse stirring.

    BER. Well, good night.
    If you do meet Horatio and Marcellus,
    The rivals° of my watch, bid them make haste.

[*Enter* HORATIO *and* MARCELLUS.]

    FRAN. I think I hear them. Stand, ho! Who is there?

15   **HOR.** Friends to this ground.

    MAR.   And liegemen to the Dane.°

    FRAN. Give you good night.

    MAR.   O, farewell, honest soldier!
    Who hath relieved you?

---

13   **rivals** partners
15   **Dane** King of Denmark

FRAN.   Bernardo hath my place.
    Give you good night.

[*Exit* FRANCISCO.]

    MAR.   Holla, Bernardo!

    BER.   Say—
    What, is Horatio there?

    HOR.   A piece of him.

20 BER.   Welcome, Horatio. Welcome, good Marcellus.

    HOR.   What, has this thing appeared again to-night?

    BER.   I have seen nothing.

    MAR.   Horatio says 'tis but our fantasy,
    And will not let belief take hold of him
25 Touching this dreaded sight twice seen of us.
    Therefore I have entreated him along
    With us to watch the minutes of this night,
    That if again this apparition come,
    He may approve° our eyes and speak to it.

30 HOR.   Tush, tush, 'twill not appear.

    BER.   Sit down awhile,
    And let us once again assail your ears,
    That are so fortified against our story,
    What we have two nights seen.

    HOR.   Well, sit we down,
    And let us hear Bernardo speak of this.

35 BER.   Last night of all,
    When yond same star that's westward from the pole°
    Had made his course t' illume that part of heaven
    Where now it burns, Marcellus and myself,
    The bell then beating one—

[*Enter* GHOST.]

40 MAR.   Peace, break thee off. Look where it comes again.

    BER.   In the same figure like the king that's dead.

    MAR.   Thou art a scholar; speak to it, Horatio.

---

29   **approve** confirm
36   **pole** polestar

BER. Looks 'a not like the king? Mark it, Horatio.

HOR. Most like. It harrows° me with fear and wonder.

45 BER. It would be spoke to.

MAR. Question it, Horatio.

HOR. What art thou that usurp'st this time of night
Together with that fair and warlike form
In which the majesty of buried Denmark°
Did sometimes° march? By heaven I charge thee, speak.

50 MAR. It is offended.

BER. See, it stalks away.

HOR. Stay. Speak, speak. I charge thee, speak.

[*Exit* GHOST.]

MAR. 'Tis gone and will not answer.

BER. How now, Horatio! You tremble and look pale.
Is not this something more than fantasy?
55 What think you on't?

HOR. Before my God, I might not this believe
Without the sensible° and true avouch
Of mine own eyes.

MAR. Is it not like the king?

HOR. As thou art to thyself.
60 Such was the very armor he had on
When he the ambitious Norway° combated.
So frowned he once when, in an angry parle,°
He smote the sledded Polacks° on the ice.
'Tis strange.

65 MAR. Thus twice before, and jump° at this dead hour,
With martial stalk hath he gone by our watch.

44	**harrows**	afflicts, distresses
48	**buried Denmark**	the buried King of Denmark
49	**sometimes**	formerly
57	**sensible**	confirmed by one of the senses
61	**Norway**	King of Norway
62	**parle**	parley
63	**sledded Polacks**	the Poles mounted on sleds or sledges
65	**jump**	just, exactly

HOR.   In what particular thought to work I know not,
But in the gross and scope° of mine opinion,
This bodes some strange eruption to our state.

70   **MAR.**   Good now, sit down, and tell me he that knows,
Why this same strict and most observant watch
So nightly toils° the subject° of the land,
And why such daily cast of brazen cannon
And foreign mart° for implements of war;
75   Why such impress° of shipwrights, whose sore task
Does not divide the Sunday from the week.
What might be toward° that this sweaty haste
Doth make the night joint-laborer with the day?
Who is't that can inform me?

HOR.   That can I.
80   At least, the whisper goes so. Our last king,
Whose image even but now appeared to us,
Was as you know by Fortinbras of Norway,
Thereto pricked on by a most emulate° pride,
Dared to the combat; in which our valiant Hamlet
85   (For so this side of our known world esteemed him)
Did slay this Fortinbras; who by a sealed compact
Well ratified by law and heraldry,°
Did forfeit, with his life, all those his lands
Which he stood seized° of, to the conqueror;
90   Against the which a moiety competent°
Was gagéd° by our king; which had returned
To the inheritance of Fortinbras,
Had he been vanquisher; as, by the same comart°

---

68   **gross and scope** general drift
72   **toils** causes to toil
      subject people
74   **mart** traffic, bargaining
75   **impress** conscription
77   **toward** imminent, impending
83   **emulate** ambitious
87   **heraldry** the law of arms, regulating tournaments and state combats
89   **seized** possessed
90   **moiety competent** sufficient portion
91   **gaged** pledged
93   **comart** joint bargain

And carriage° of the article designed,
95   His fell to Hamlet. Now, sir, young Fortinbras,
Of unimprovéd° mettle hot and full,
Hath in the skirts of Norway here and there
Sharked up° a list of lawless resolutes
For food and diet to some enterprise
100   That hath a stomach° in't; which is no other,
As it doth well appear unto our state,
But to recover of us by strong hand
And terms compulsatory, those foresaid lands
So by his father lost; and this, I take it,
105   Is the main motive of our preparations,
The source of this our watch, and the chief head°
Of this post-haste and romage° in the land.

BER.   I think it be no other but e'en so.
Well may it sort° that this portentous figure
110   Comes arméd through our watch so like the king
That was and is the question of these wars.

HOR.   A mote° it is to trouble the mind's eye.
In the most high and palmy° state of Rome,
A little ere the mightiest Julius fell,
115   The graves stood tenantless, and the sheeted° dead
Did squeak and gibber in the Roman streets;
As stars with trains of fire, and dews of blood,
Disasters° in the sun; and the moist star,°
Upon whose influence Neptune's empire stands,
120   Was sick almost to doomsday with eclipse.

---

  94   **carriage** import
  96   **unimproved** unrestrained
  98   **Sharked up** picked up indiscriminately
 100   **stomach** spice of adventure
 106   **head** fountainhead
 107   **romage** turmoil
 109   **sort** suit, be in accordance
 112   **mote** particle of dust
 113   **palmy** flourishing
 115   **sheeted** in shrouds
 118   **Disasters** ominous signs
      moist star the moon

And even the like precurse° of feared events,
As harbingers° preceding still° the fates
And prologue to the omen° coming on,
Have heaven and earth together demonstrated
125 Unto our climatures° and countrymen.

[*Enter* GHOST.]

But soft, behold, lo where it comes again!
I'll cross it° though it blast me.—Stay, illusion.

[GHOST *spreads his arms.*]

If thou hast any sound or use of voice,
Speak to me.
130 If there be any good thing to be done,
That may to thee do ease, and grace to me,
Speak to me.
If thou art privy to thy country's fate,
Which happily° foreknowing may avoid,
135 O, speak!
Or if thou hast uphoarded in thy life
Extorted treasure in the womb of earth,
For which, they say, you spirits oft walk in death,

[*The cock crows.*]

Speak of it. Stay, and speak. Stop it, Marcellus.

140 **MAR.** Shall I strike at it with my partisan?°

HOR. Do, if it will not stand.

BER.   'Tis here.

HOR.   'Tis here.

MAR. 'Tis gone.

[*Exit* GHOST.]

We do it wrong, being so majestical,

To offer it the show of violence;
For it is as the air, invulnerable,
And our vain blows malicious mockery.

BER.   It was about to speak when the cock crew.

HOR.   And then it started like a guilty thing
Upon a fearful summons. I have heard
The cock, that is the trumpet to the morn,
Doth with his lofty and shrill-sounding throat
Awake the god of day, and at his warning,
Whether in sea or fire, in earth or air,
Th' extravagant° and erring° spirit hies
To his confine; and of the truth herein
This present object made probation.°

MAR.   It faded on the crowing of the cock.
Some say that ever 'gainst° that season comes
Wherein our Savior's birth is celebrated,
This bird of dawning singeth all night long,
And then, they say, no spirit dare stir abroad,
The nights are wholesome, then no planets strike,°
No fairy takes,° nor witch hath power to charm,
So hallowed and so gracious is that time.

HOR.   So have I heard and do in part believe it.
But look, the morn in russet mantle clad
Walks o'er the dew of yon high eastward hill.
Break we our watch up, and by my advice
Let us impart what we have seen to-night
Unto young Hamlet, for upon my life
This spirit, dumb to us, will speak to him.
Do you consent we shall acquaint him with it,
As needful in our loves, fitting our duty?

MAR.   Let's do't, I pray, and I this morning know
Where we shall find him most convenient.

[*Exeunt.*]

154	**extravagant** straying, vagrant	
	erring wandering	
156	**probation** proof	
158	**'gainst** just before	
162	**strike** blast, destroy by malign influence	
163	**takes** bewitches	

Scene 2

[*Flourish. Enter* CLAUDIUS KING OF DENMARK, GERTRUDE THE QUEEN, COUNCILLORS *including* POLONIUS, *and his son* LAERTES, HAMLET, *cum aliis*° *including* VOLTEMAND *and* CORNELIUS.]

    KING.   Though yet of Hamlet our dear brother's death
        The memory be green, and that it us befitted
        To bear our hearts in grief, and our whole kingdom
        To be contracted in one brow of woe,
5   Yet so far hath discretion fought with nature
        That we with wisest sorrow think on him,
        Together with remembrance of ourselves.
        Therefore our sometime sister, now our queen,
        Th' imperial jointress° to this warlike state,
10   Have we, as 'twere with a defeated joy,
        With an auspicious and a dropping eye,
        With mirth in funeral, and with dirge in marriage,
        In equal scale weighing delight and dole,
        Taken to wife; nor have we herein barred°
15   Your better wisdoms, which have freely gone
        With this affair along. For all, our thanks.
        Now follows that you know young Fortinbras,
        Holding a weak supposal of our worth,
        Or thinking by our late dear brother's death
20   Our state to be disjoint and out of frame,
        Colleaguéd° with this dream of his advantage,
        He hath not failed to pester us with message
        Importing the surrender of those lands
        Lost by his father, with all bands of law,
25   To our most valiant brother. So much for him.
        Now for ourself, and for this time of meeting,
        Thus much the business is: we have here writ
        To Norway, uncle of young Fortinbras—
        Who, impotent and bedrid, scarcely hears
30   Of this his nephew's purpose—to suppress
        His further gait° herein, in that the levies,

0.2   **cum aliis** with others
9   **jointress** a widow who holds a jointure or life interest in an estate
14   **barred** excluded
21   **Colleagued** united
31   **gait** proceeding

The lists, and full proportions° are all made
Out of his subject; and we here dispatch
You, good Cornelius, and you, Voltemand,
35   For bearers of this greeting to old Norway,
Giving to you no further personal power
To business with the king, more than the scope
Of these delated° articles allow.
Farewell, and let your haste commend your duty.

COR. ⎫
40   ⎬ In that, and all things will we show our duty.
VOL. ⎭

KING.   We doubt it nothing, heartily farewell.

[*Exeunt VOLTEMAND and CORNELIUS.*]

And now, Laertes, what's the news with you?
You told us of some suit. What is't, Laertes?
You cannot speak of reason to the Dane°
45   And lose your voice.° What wouldst thou beg, Laertes,
That shall not be my offer, not thy asking?
The head is not more native° to the heart,
The hand more instrumental° to the mouth,
Than is the throne of Denmark to thy father.
50   What wouldst thou have, Laertes?

LAER.   My dread lord,
Your leave and favor to return to France,
From whence, though willingly, I came to Denmark
To show my duty in your coronation,
Yet now I must confess, that duty done,
55   My thoughts and wishes bend again toward France,
And bow them to your gracious leave and pardon.°

KING.   Have you your father's leave? What says Polonius?

POL.   He hath, my lord, wrung from me my slow leave
By laborsome petition, and at last

---

32   **proportions** forces or supplies for war
38   **delated** expressly stated
44   **Dane** King of Denmark
45   **lose your voice** speak in vain
47   **native** joined by nature
48   **instrumental** serviceable
56   **pardon** indulgence

60   Upon his will I sealed my hard° consent.
        I do beseech you give him leave to go.

     KING.   Take thy fair hour, Laertes. Time be thine,
        And thy best graces spend it at thy will.
        But now, my cousin° Hamlet, and my son—

65   **HAM.**   [*Aside*.] A little more than kin,° and less than kind.°

     KING.   How is it that the clouds still hang on you?

     HAM.   Not so, my lord. I am too much in the sun.

     QUEEN.   Good Hamlet, cast thy nighted color off,
        And let thine eye look like a friend on Denmark.
70   Do not for ever with thy vailéd° lids
        Seek for thy noble father in the dust.
        Thou know'st 'tis common—all that lives must die,
        Passing through nature to eternity.

     HAM.   Ay, madam, it is common.

     QUEEN.   If it be,
75   Why seems it so particular° with thee?

     HAM.   Seems, madam? Nay, it is. I know not 'seems.'
        'Tis not alone my inky cloak, good mother,
        Nor customary suits of solemn black,
        Nor windy suspiration of forced breath,
80   No, nor the fruitful river in the eye,
        Nor the dejected haviour of the visage,
        Together with all forms, moods, shapes of grief,
        That can denote me truly. These indeed seem,
        For they are actions that a man might play,
85   But I have that within which passes show—
        These but the trappings and the suits of woe.

     KING.   'Tis sweet and commendable in your nature, Hamlet,
        To give these mourning duties to your father,
        But you must know your father lost a father,
90   That father lost, lost his, and the survivor bound

---

    60   **hard** reluctant
    64   **cousin** kinsman of any kind except parent, child, brother, or sister
    65   **kin** related as nephew
          kind (1) affectionate (2) natural, lawful
    70   **vailed** lowered
    75   **particular** personal, individual

In filial obligation for some term
To do obsequious° sorrow. But to persever°
In obstinate condolement is a course
Of impious stubbornness. 'Tis unmanly grief.

95   It shows a will most incorrect to heaven,
A heart unfortified, a mind impatient,
An understanding simple and unschooled.
For what we know must be, and is as common
As any the most vulgar thing to sense,

100   Why should we in our peevish opposition
Take it to heart? Fie, 'tis a fault to heaven,
A fault against the dead, a fault to nature,
To reason most absurd, whose common theme
Is death of fathers, and who still hath cried,

105   From the first corse° till he that died to-day,
'This must be so.' We pray you throw to earth
This unprevailing woe, and think of us
As of a father, for let the world take note
You are the most immediate to our throne,

110   And with no less nobility of love
Than that which dearest father bears his son
Do I impart toward you. For your intent
In going back to school in Wittenberg,
It is most retrograde° to our desire,

115   And we beseech you, bend you to remain
Here in the cheer and comfort of our eye,
Our chiefest courtier, cousin, and our son.

QUEEN.   Let not thy mother lose her prayers, Hamlet.
I pray thee stay with us, go not to Wittenberg.

120   HAM.   I shall in all my best obey you, madam.

KING.   Why, 'tis a loving and a fair reply.
Be as ourself in Denmark. Madam, come.
This gentle and unforced accord of Hamlet
Sits smiling to my heart, in grace whereof,

125   No jocund health that Denmark drinks to-day

---

92   **obsequious** dutiful in performing funeral obsequies or manifesting regard for the dead
persever persevere

105   **corse** corpse

114   **retrograde** contrary

But the great cannon to the clouds shall tell,
And the king's rouse° the heaven shall bruit° again,
Respeaking earthly thunder. Come away.

[*Flourish. Exeunt all but* HAMLET.]

     HAM.   O, that this too too sallied° flesh would melt,
130   Thaw, and resolve itself into a dew,
         Or that the Everlasting had not fixed
         His canon° 'gainst self-slaughter. O God, God,
         How weary, stale, flat, and unprofitable
         Seem to me all the uses of this world!
135   Fie on't, ah, fie, 'tis an unweeded garden
         That grows to seed. Things rank and gross in nature
         Possess it merely.° That it should come to this,
         But two months dead, nay, not so much, not two.
         So excellent a king, that was to this
140   Hyperion° to a satyr, so loving to my mother,
         That he might not beteem° the winds of heaven
         Visit her face too roughly. Heaven and earth,
         Must I remember? Why, she would hang on him
         As if increase of appetite had grown
145   By what it fed on, and yet, within a month—
         Let me not think on't. Frailty, thy name is woman—
         A little month, or ere those shoes were old
         With which she followed my poor father's body
         Like Niobe,° all tears, why she—

---

127   **rouse** full draught of liquor
        bruit echo
129   **sallied** sullied
132   **canon** law
137   **merely** entirely
140   **Hyperion** the sun god
141   **beteem** allow
149   **Niobe** wife of Amphion, King of Thebes, she boasted of having more children than Leto and was punished when her seven sons and seven daughters were slain by Apollo and Artemis, children of Leto; in her grief she was changed by Zeus into a stone, which continually dropped tears

150   O God, a beast that wants° discourse of reason°
        Would have mourned longer—married with my uncle,
        My father's brother, but no more like my father
        Than I to Hercules. Within a month,
        Ere yet the salt of most unrighteous tears
155   Had left the flushing in her galléd° eyes,
        She married. O, most wicked speed, to post
        With such dexterity to incestuous sheets!
        It is not, nor it cannot come to good.
        But break my heart, for I must hold my tongue.

[*Enter* HORATIO, MARCELLUS, *and* BERNARDO.]

160   **HOR.**   Hail to your lordship!

        HAM.   I am glad to see you well.
        Horatio—or I do forget myself.

        HOR.   The same, my lord, and your poor servant ever.

        HAM.   Sir, my good friend, I'll change° that name with you.
        And what make° you from Wittenberg, Horatio?
165   Marcellus?

        MAR.   My good lord!

        HAM.   I am very glad to see you. [*To* BERNARDO.] Good even, sir.—
        But what, in faith, make you from Wittenberg?

        HOR.   A truant disposition, good my lord.

170   **HAM.**   I would not hear your enemy say so,
        Nor shall you do my ear that violence
        To make it truster of your own report
        Against yourself. I know you are no truant.
        But what is your affair in Elsinore?
175   We'll teach you to drink deep ere you depart.

        HOR.   My lord, I came to see your father's funeral.

        HAM.   I prithee do not mock me, fellow-student,
        I think it was to see my mother's wedding.

        HOR.   Indeed, my lord, it followed hard upon.

---

150   **wants** lacks
        discourse of reason the reasoning faculty
155   **galled** sore from rubbing or chafing
163   **change** exchange
164   **make** do

180   **HAM.**   Thrift, thrift, Horatio. The funeral baked meats
Did coldly furnish forth the marriage tables.
Would I had met my dearest° foe in heaven
Or ever I had seen that day, Horatio!
My father—methinks I see my father.

185   **HOR.**   Where, my lord?

   HAM.   In my mind's eye, Horatio.

   HOR.   I saw him once, 'a was a goodly king.

   HAM.   'A was a man, take him for all in all,
I shall not look upon his like again.

   HOR.   My lord, I think I saw him yesternight.

190   **HAM.**   Saw who?

   HOR.   My lord, the king your father.

   HAM.   The king my father?

   HOR.   Season° your admiration° for a while
With an attent ear till I may deliver
Upon the witness of these gentlemen
195   This marvel to you.

   HAM.   For God's love, let me hear!

   HOR.   Two nights together had these gentlemen,
Marcellus and Bernardo, on their watch
In the dead waste and middle of the night
Been thus encountered. A figure like your father,
200   Armed at point exactly,° cap-a-pe,°
Appears before them, and with solemn march
Goes slow and stately by them. Thrice he walked
By their oppressed and fear-surprisèd eyes
Within his truncheon's° length, whilst they, distilled
205   Almost to jelly with the act of fear,
Stand dumb and speak not to him. This to me
In dreadful secrecy impart they did,

---

182   **dearest** direst
192   **Season** temper, moderate
       admiration wonder, astonishment
200   **at point exactly** in every particular
       cap-a-pe from head to foot
204   **truncheon** military leader's baton

And I with them the third night kept the watch,
Where, as they had delivered, both in time,
210 Form of the thing, each word made true and good,
The apparition comes. I knew your father.
These hands are not more like.

HAM.   But where was this?

MAR.   My lord, upon the platform where we watch.

HAM.   Did you not speak to it?

HOR.   My lord, I did,
215 But answer made it none. Yet once methought
It lifted up it° head and did address
Itself to motion, like as it would speak;
But even then the morning cock crew loud,
And at the sound it shrunk in haste away
220 And vanished from our sight.

HAM.   'Tis very strange.

HOR.   As I do live, my honored lord, 'tis true,
And we did think it writ down in our duty
To let you know of it.

HAM.   Indeed, sirs, but
This troubles me. Hold you the watch to-night?

225 ALL.   We do, my lord.

HAM.   Armed, say you?

ALL.   Armed, my lord.

HAM.   From top to toe?

ALL.   My lord, from head to foot.

HAM.   Then saw you not his face.

HOR.   O yes, my lord, he wore his beaver° up.

HAM.   What, looked he frowningly?

230 HOR.   A countenance more in sorrow than in anger.

HAM.   Pale or red?

HOR.   Nay, very pale.

HAM.   And fixed his eyes upon you?

---

216   **it** its

228   **beaver** the part of the helmet that was drawn down to cover the face

HOR.   Most constantly.

HAM.   I would I had been there.

HOR.   It would have much amazed you.

HAM.   Very like.
235   Stayed it long?

HOR.   While one with moderate haste might tell° a
          hundred.

BOTH.   Longer, longer.

HOR.   Not when I saw't.

HAM.   His beard was grizzled,° no?

HOR.   It was as I have seen it in his life,
          A sable silvered.°

HAM.   I will watch to-night.
240   Perchance 'twill walk again.

HOR.   I warr'nt it will.

HAM.   If it assume my noble father's person,
          I'll speak to it though hell itself should gape
          And bid me hold my peace. I pray you all,
          If you have hitherto concealed this sight,
245   Let it be tenable° in your silence still,
          And whatsomever° else shall hap to-night,
          Give it an understanding but no tongue.
          I will requite your loves. So fare you well.
          Upon the platform 'twixt eleven and twelve
250   I'll visit you.

ALL.   Our duty to your honor.

HAM.   Your loves, as mine to you. Farewell.

---

235   **tell** count
237   **grizzled** grayish
239   **sable silvered** black mixed with white
245   **tenable** retained
246   **whatsomever** whatsoever

My father's spirit in arms? All is not well.
I doubt° some foul play. Would the night were come!
Till then sit still, my soul. Foul deeds will rise,
255   Though all the earth o'erwhelm them, to men's eyes.

[Exit.]

Scene 3

[Enter LAERTES and OPHELIA his sister.]

LAER.   My necessaries are embarked. Farewell.
And, sister, as the winds give benefit
And convoy is assistant, do not sleep,
But let me hear from you.

OPH.   Do you doubt that?

5   **LAER.**   For Hamlet, and the trifling of his favor,
Hold it a fashion° and a toy in blood,°
A violet in the youth of primy° nature,
Forward, not permanent, sweet, not lasting,
The perfume and suppliance of a minute,
10   No more.

OPH.   No more but so?

LAER.   Think it no more.
For nature crescent° does not grow alone
In thews° and bulk, but as this temple° waxes
The inward service of the mind and soul
Grows wide withal. Perhaps he loves you now,
15   And now no soil nor cautel° doth besmirch
The virtue of his will,° but you must fear,

---

253   **doubt** suspect
6   **fashion** the creation of a season only
   toy in blood passing fancy
7   **primy** of the springtime
11   **crescent** growing
12   **thews** sinews, strength
   this temple the body
15   **cautel** deceit
16   **will** desire

His greatness weighed,° his will is not his own,
For he himself is subject to his birth.
He may not, as unvalued persons° do,
20 Carve for himself,° for on his choice depends
The safety and health of this whole state,
And therefore must his choice be circumscribed
Unto the voice and yielding° of that body
Whereof he is the head. Then if he says he loves you,
25 It fits your wisdom so far to believe it
As he in his particular act and place
May give his saying deed, which is no further
Than the main voice of Denmark goes withal.
Then weigh what loss your honor may sustain
30 If with too credent° ear you list his songs,
Or lose your heart, or your chaste treasure open
To his unmastered importunity.
Fear it, Ophelia, fear it, my dear sister,
And keep you in the rear of your affection,°
35 Out of the shot and danger of desire.
The chariest maid is prodigal enough
If she unmask her beauty to the moon.
Virtue itself scapes not calumnious strokes.
The canker° galls° the infants of the spring
40 Too oft before their buttons° be disclosed,
And in the morn and liquid dew of youth
Contagious blastments° are most imminent.
Be wary then; best safety lies in fear.
Youth to itself rebels, though none else near.

45 **OPH.** I shall the effect of this good lesson keep
As watchman to my heart. But, good my brother,
Do not as some ungracious pastors do,

17	**greatness weighed** high position considered
19	**unvalued persons** persons of no social importance
20	**Carve for himself** act according to his own inclination
23	**yielding** assent
30	**credent** trusting
34	**affection** feeling
39	**canker** canker-worm (which feeds on roses)
	galls injures
40	**buttons** buds
42	**blastments** blights

Show me the steep and thorny way to heaven,
Whiles like a puffed and reckless libertine
50 Himself the primrose path of dalliance treads
And recks° not his own rede.°

LAER.   O, fear me not.

[*Enter* POLONIUS.]

I stay too long. But here my father comes.
A double blessing is a double grace;
Occasion smiles upon a second leave.

55 POL.   Yet here, Laertes? Aboard, aboard, for shame!
The wind sits in the shoulder of your sail,
And you are stayed for. There, my blessing with thee,
And these few precepts in thy memory
Look thou character.° Give thy thoughts no tongue,
60 Nor any unproportioned° thought his act.
Be thou familiar, but by no means vulgar.°
Those friends thou hast, and their adoption tried,
Grapple them unto thy soul with hoops of steel,
But do not dull thy palm with entertainment
65 Of each new-hatched, unfledged courage.° Beware
Of entrance to a quarrel, but being in,
Bear't that th' opposéd may beware of thee.
Give every man thy ear, but few thy voice;
Take each man's censure, but reserve thy judgment.
70 Costly thy habit as thy purse can buy,
But not expressed in fancy; rich not gaudy,
For the apparel oft proclaims the man,
And they in France of the best rank and station
Are of a most select and generous chief° in that.
75 Neither a borrower nor a lender be,
For loan oft loses both itself and friend,
And borrowing dulls th' edge of husbandry.°

---

51 **recks** regards
    rede counsel
59 **character** engrave
60 **unproportioned** inordinate
61 **vulgar** common
65 **courage** young blood, man of spirit
74 **chief** eminence
77 **husbandry** thriftiness

This above all, to thine own self be true,
And it must follow as the night the day
80 Thou canst not then be false to any man.
Farewell. My blessing season° this in thee!

LAER.   Most humbly do I take my leave, my lord.

POL.   The time invites you. Go, your servants tend.°

LAER.   Farewell, Ophelia, and remember well
85 What I have said to you.

OPH.   'Tis in my memory locked,
And you yourself shall keep the key of it.

LAER.   Farewell.

[*Exit LAERTES.*]

POL.   What is't, Ophelia, he hath said to you?

OPH.   So please you, something touching the Lord Hamlet.

90 POL.   Marry,° well bethought.
'Tis told me he hath very oft of late
Given private time to you, and you yourself
Have of your audience been most free and bounteous.
If it be so—as so 'tis put on me,
95 And that in way of caution—I must tell you,
You do not understand yourself so clearly
As it behooves my daughter and your honor.
What is between you? Give me up the truth.

OPH.   He hath, my lord, of late made many tenders°
100 Of his affection to me.

POL.   Affection? Pooh! You speak like a green girl,
Unsifted° in such perilous circumstance.
Do you believe his tenders, as you call them?

OPH.   I do not know, my lord, what I should think.

105 POLL.   Marry, I will teach you. Think yourself a baby
That you have ta'en these tenders for true pay
Which are not sterling. Tender yourself more dearly,

---

81   **season** ripen
83   **tend** attend, wait
90   **Marry** by Mary
99   **tenders** offers
102   **Unsifted** untried

Or (not to crack the wind of the poor phrase,
Running it thus) you'll tender me a fool.

110 **OPH.** My lord, he hath importuned me with love
In honorable fashion.

POL. Ay, fashion you may call it. Go to, go to.

OPH. And hath given countenance to his speech, my lord,
With almost all the holy vows of heaven.

115 **POL.** Ay, springes° to catch woodcocks. I do know,
When the blood burns, how prodigal the soul
Lends the tongue vows. These blazes, daughter,
Giving more light than heat, extinct in both
Even in their promise, as it is a-making,
120 You must not take for fire. From this time
Be something scanter of your maiden presence.
Set your entreatments° at a higher rate
Than a command to parle. For Lord Hamlet,
Believe so much in him that he is young,
125 And with a larger tether may he walk
Than may be given you. In few, Ophelia,
Do not believe his vows, for they are brokers,°
Not of that dye which their investments° show,
But mere implorators° of unholy suits,
130 Breathing like sanctified and pious bawds,
The better to beguile. This is for all:
I would not, in plain terms, from this time forth
Have you so slander any moment leisure
As to give words or talk with the Lord Hamlet.
135 Look to't, I charge you. Come your ways.

OPH. I shall obey, my lord.

[*Exeunt.*]

---

115   **springes** snares
122   **entreatments** military negotiations for a surrender
127   **brokers** go-betweens
128   **investments** clothes
129   **implorators** solicitors

Scene 4

[*Enter* HAMLET, HORATIO, *and* MARCELLUS.]

HAM. The air bites shrewdly; it is very cold.

HOR. It is a nipping and an eager° air.

HAM. What hour now?

HOR. I think it lacks of twelve.

MAR. No, it is struck.

5   **HOR.** Indeed? I heard it not. It then draws near the season
          Wherein the spirit held his wont to walk.

[*A flourish of trumpets, and two pieces go off.*]

          What does this mean, my lord?

HAM. The king doth wake to-night and take his rouse,
          Keeps wassail,° and the swagg'ring up-spring° reels,
10   And as he drains his draughts of Rhenish down,
          The kettledrum and trumpet thus bray out
          The triumph of his pledge.

HOR. Is it a custom?

HAM. Ay, marry, is't,
          But to my mind, though I am native here
15   And to the manner born, it is a custom
          More honored in the breach than the observance.
          This heavy-headed revel east and west
          Makes us traduced and taxed of° other nations.
          They clepe° us drunkards, and with swinish phrase
20   Soil our addition,° and indeed it takes
          From our achievements, though performed at height,
          The pith and marrow of our attribute.°
          So oft it chances in particular men,
          That for some vicious mole of nature in them,
25   As in their birth, wherein they are not guilty

---

2   **eager** sharp
9   **wassail** carousal
     up-spring a German dance
18 **taxed of** censured by
19 **clepe** call
20 **addition** title added to a man's name to denote his rank
22 **attribute** reputation

(Since nature cannot choose his° origin),
By the o'ergrowth of some complexion,°
Oft breaking down the pales and forts of reason,
Or by some habit that too much o'er-leavens°
30   The form of plausive° manners—that these men,
Carrying, I say, the stamp of one defect,
Being nature's livery° or fortune's star,°
His virtues else, be they as pure as grace,
As infinite as man may undergo,
35   Shall in the general censure take corruption
From that particular fault. The dram of evil
Doth all the noble substance often doubt°
To his° own scandal.

[*Enter* GHOST.]

HOR.   Look, my lord, it comes.
HAM.   Angels and ministers of grace defend us!
40   Be thou a spirit of health or goblin damned,
Bring with thee airs from heaven or blasts from hell,
Be thy intents wicked or charitable,
Thou com'st in such a questionable shape
That I will speak to thee. I'll call thee Hamlet,
45   King, father, royal Dane. O, answer me!
Let me not burst in ignorance, but tell
Why thy canonized° bones, hearséd° in death,
Have burst their cerements; why the sepulchre
Wherein we saw thee quietly interred
50   Hath oped his ponderous and marble jaws
To cast thee up again. What may this mean
That thou, dead corse, again in complete steel
Revisits thus the glimpses of the moon,

---

26   **his** its
27   **complexion** one of the four temperaments (sanguine, melancholy, choleric, and phlegmatic)
29   **o'er-leavens** works change throughout
30   **plausive** pleasing
32   **livery** badge
       star a person's fortune, rank, or destiny, viewed as determined by the stars
37   **doubt** put out, obliterate
38   **his** its
47   **canonized** buried according to the church's rule
       hearsed coffined, buried

Making night hideous, and we fools of nature
55 So horridly to shake our disposition
With thoughts beyond the reaches of our souls?
Say, why is this? wherefore? What should we do?

[GHOST *beckons.*]

HOR.   It beckons you to go away with it,
As if it some impartment° did desire
60 To you alone.

MAR.   Look with what courteous action
It waves you to a more removéd ground.
But do not go with it.

HOR.   No, by no means.

HAM.   It will not speak; then I will follow it.

HOR.   Do not, my lord.

HAM.   Why, what should be the fear?
65 I do not set my life at a pin's fee,
And for my soul, what can it do to that,
Being a thing immortal as itself?
It waves me forth again. I'll follow it.

HOR.   What if it tempt you toward the flood, my lord,
70 Or to the dreadful summit of the cliff
That beetles° o'er his base into the sea,
And there assume some other horrible form,
Which might deprive your sovereignty of reason°
And draw you into madness? Think of it.
75 The very place puts toys° of desperation,
Without more motive, into every brain
That looks so many fathoms to the sea
And hears it roar beneath.

HAM.   It waves me still.
Go on. I'll follow thee.

80 **MAR.**   You shall not go, my lord.

HAM.   Hold off your hands.

---

59   **impartment** communication
71   **beetles** juts out
73   **sovereignty of reason** state of being ruled by reason
75   **toys** fancies, impules

HOR.	Be ruled, You shall not go.

HAM.   My fate cries out
And makes each petty artere° in this body
As hardy as the Nemean lion's° nerve.
Still am I called. Unhand me, gentlemen.
85   By heaven, I'll make a ghost of him that lets° me.
I say, away!—Go on. I'll follow thee.

[*Exeunt* GHOST *and* HAMLET.]

HOR.   He waxes desperate with imagination.

MAR.   Let's follow. 'Tis not fit thus to obey him.

HOR.   Have after. To what issue will this come?

90   **MAR.**   Something is rotten in the state of Denmark.

HOR.   Heaven will direct it.

MAR.   Nay, let's follow him.

[*Exeunt.*]

Scene 5

[*Enter* GHOST *and* HAMLET.]

HAM.   Whither wilt thou lead me? Speak. I'll go no further.
GHOST.   Mark me.
HAM.   I will.
GHOST.   My hour is almost come
When I to sulph'rous and tormenting flames
Must render up myself.
HAM.   Alas, poor ghost!
5   **GHOST.**   Pity me not, but lend thy serious hearing
To what I shall unfold.
HAM.   Speak. I am bound to hear.
GHOST.   So art thou to revenge, when thou shalt hear.
HAM.   What?
GHOST.   I am thy father's spirit,
10   Doomed for a certain term to walk the night,
And for the day confined to fast in fires,

---

82   **artere** artery
83   **Nemean lion** slain by Hercules in the performance of one of his twelve labors
85   **lets** hinders

Till the foul crimes done in my days of nature
Are burnt and purged away. But that I am forbid
To tell the secrets of my prison house,

15   I could a tale unfold whose lightest word
Would harrow up thy soul, freeze thy young blood,
Make thy two eyes like stars start from their spheres,
Thy knotted and combinéd locks to part,
And each particular hair to stand an° end,

20   Like quills upon the fretful porpentine.°
But this eternal blazon° must not be
To ears of flesh and blood. List, list, O, list!
If thou didst ever thy dear father love—

HAM.   O God!

25   **GHOST.**   Revenge his foul and most unnatural murder.

HAM.   Murder!

GHOST.   Murder most foul, as in the best it is,
But this most foul, strange, and unnatural.

HAM.   Haste me to know't, that I, with wings as swift

30   As meditation or the thoughts of love,
May sweep to my revenge.

GHOST.   I find thee apt,
And duller shouldst thou be than the fat weed
That roots itself in ease on Lethe° wharf,
Wouldst thou not stir in this. Now, Hamlet, hear.

35   'Tis given out that, sleeping in my orchard,
A serpent stung me. So the whole ear of Denmark
Is by a forgéd process° of my death
Rankly abused. But know, thou noble youth,
The serpent that did sting thy father's life

40   Now wears his crown.

HAM.   O my prophetic soul!
My uncle!

GHOST.   Ay, that incestuous, that adulterate beast,
With witchcraft of his wits, with traitorous gifts—

---

19   **an** on
20   **porpentine** porcupine
21   **eternal blazon** proclamation of the secrets of eternity
33   **Lethe** the river in Hades that brings forgetfulness
37   **process** account

O wicked wit and gifts that have the power
45 So to seduce!—won to his shameful lust
The will of my most seeming virtuous queen.
O Hamlet, what a falling off was there,
From me, whose love was of that dignity
That it went hand in hand even with the vow
50 I made to her in marriage, and to decline
Upon a wretch whose natural gifts were poor
To those of mine!
But virtue, as it never will be moved,
Though lewdness court it in a shape of heaven,
55 So lust, though to a radiant angel linked,
Will sate itself in a celestial bed
And prey on garbage.
But soft, methinks I scent the morning air.
Brief let me be. Sleeping within my orchard,
60 My custom always of the afternoon,
Upon my secure° hour thy uncle stole,
With juice of cursed hebona° in a vial,
And in the porches of my ears did pour
The leperous distilment, whose effect
65 Holds such an enmity with blood of man
That swift as quicksilver it courses through
The natural gates and alleys of the body,
And with a sudden vigor it doth posset°
And curd, like eager° droppings into milk,
70 The thin and wholesome blood. So did it mine,
And a most instant tetter° barked° about
Most lazar-like with vile and loathsome crust
All my smooth body.
Thus was I sleeping by a brother's hand
75 Of life, of crown, of queen at once dispatched,
Cut off even in the blossoms of my sin,

---

61 **secure** free from suspicion
62 **hebona** an imaginary poison, associated with henbane
68 **posset** curdle
69 **eager** acid
71 **tetter** a skin eruption
   barked covered as with bark

Unhouseled,° disappointed,° unaneled,°
No reck'ning made, but sent to my account
With all my imperfections on my head.
80 O, horrible! O, horrible! most horrible!
If thou hast nature in thee, bear it not.
Let not the royal bed of Denmark be
A couch for luxury° and damnéd incest.
But howsomever thou pursues this act,
85 Taint not thy mind, nor let thy soul contrive
Against thy mother aught. Leave her to heaven,
And to those thorns that in her bosom lodge
To prick and sting her. Fare thee well at once.
The glowworm shows the matin° to be near,
90 And gins to pale his uneffectual fire.
Adieu, adieu, adieu. Remember me.

[*Exit.*]

HAM. O all you host of heaven! O earth! What else?
And shall I couple hell? O, fie! Hold, hold, my heart,
And you, my sinews, grow not instant old,
95 But bear me stiffly up. Remember thee?
Ay, thou poor ghost, whiles memory holds a seat
In this distracted globe.° Remember thee?
Yea, from the table° of my memory
I'll wipe away all trivial fond° records,
100 All saws° of books, all forms,° all pressures° past
That youth and observation copied there,
And thy commandment all alone shall live
Within the book and volume of my brain,
Unmixed with baser matter. Yes, by heaven!

---

77 **Unhouseled** without having received the sacrament
disappointed unprepared
unaneled without extreme unction
83 **luxury** lust
89 **matin** morning
97 **globe** head
98 **table** writing tablet, memorandum book (as at line 107, below; here metaphorically of the mind)
99 **fond** foolish
100 **saws** sayings
forms concepts
pressures impressions

105   O most pernicious woman!
      O villain, villain, smiling, damnéd villain!
      My tables—meet it is I set it down
      That one may smile, and smile, and be a villain.
      At least I am sure it may be so in Denmark. [*Writing.*]
110   So, uncle, there you are. Now to my word:
      It is 'Adieu, adieu. Remember me.'
      I have sworn't.

[*Enter* HORATIO *and* MARCELLUS.]

      HOR.   My lord, my lord!

      MAR.   Lord Hamlet!

      HOR.   Heavens secure him!

      HAM.   So be it!

115   MAR.   Illo, ho, ho,° my lord!

      HAM.   Hillo, ho, ho, boy! Come, bird, come.

      MAR.   How is't, my noble lord?

      HOR.   What news, my lord?

      HAM.   O, wonderful!

      HOR.   Good my lord, tell it.

      HAM.   No, you will reveal it.

120   HOR.   Not I, my lord, by heaven.

      MAR.   Nor I, my lord.

      HAM.   How say you then, would heart of man once think it?
             But you'll be secret?

      BOTH.   Ay, by heaven, my lord.

      HAM.   There's never a villain dwelling in all Denmark
             But he's an arrant knave.

125   HOR.   There needs no ghost, my lord, come from the grave
             To tell us this.

      HAM.   Why, right, you are in the right,
             And so without more circumstance at all
             I hold it fit that we shake hands and part,
             You, as your business and desire shall point you,
130   For every man hath business and desire
             Such as it is, and for my own poor part,
             I will go pray.

_____

      115   **Illo, ho, ho** cry of the falconer to summon his hawk

HOR.   These are but wild and whirling words, my lord.

HAM.   I am sorry they offend you, heartily;
135   Yes, faith, heartily.

HOR.   There's no offence, my lord.

HAM.   Yes, by Saint Patrick,° but there is, Horatio,
And much offence too. Touching this vision here,
It is an honest ghost, that let me tell you.
For your desire to know what is between us,
140   O'ermaster't as you may. And now, good friends,
As you are friends, scholars, and soldiers,
Give me one poor request.

HOR.   What is't, my lord? We will.

HAM.   Never make known what you have seen to-night.

145 **BOTH.**   My lord, we will not.

HAM.   Nay, but swear't.

HOR.   In faith,
My lord, not I.

MAR.   Nor I, my lord, in faith.

HAM.   Upon my sword.

MAR.   We have sworn, my lord, already.

HAM.   Indeed, upon my sword, indeed.

[GHOST *cries under the stage.*]

GHOST.   Swear.

HAM.   Ha, ha, boy, say'st thou so? Art thou there, truepenny?°
150   Come on. You hear this fellow in the cellarage.
Consent to swear.

HOR.   Propose the oath, my lord.

HAM.   Never to speak of this that you have seen,
Swear by my sword.

GHOST.   [*Beneath.*] Swear.

155 **HAM.**   Hic et ubique?° Then we'll shift our ground.

---

136   **Saint Patrick** associated, in the late middle ages, with purgatory, whence the ghost has
      presumably come

149   **truepenny** honest fellow

155   **Hic et ubique** here and everywhere

Come hither, gentlemen,
And lay your hands again upon my sword.
Swear by my sword
Never to speak of this that you have heard.

160 **GHOST.** [*Beneath.*] Swear by his sword.

HAM. Well said, old mole! Canst work i' th' earth so fast?
A worthy pioneer!° Once more remove, good friends.

HOR. O day and night, but this is wondrous strange!

HAM. And therefore as a stranger give it welcome.
165 There are more things in heaven and earth, Horatio,
Than are dreamt of in your philosophy.
But come.
Here as before, never, so help you mercy,
How strange or odd some'er I bear myself
170 (As I perchance hereafter shall think meet
To put an antic° disposition on),
That you, at such times, seeing me, never shall,
With arms encumbered° thus, or this head-shake,
Or by pronouncing of some doubtful phrase,
175 As 'Well, well, we know', or 'We could, and if we would'
Or 'If we list to speak', or 'There be, and if they might'
Or such ambiguous giving out, to note
That you know aught of me—this do swear,
So grace and mercy at your most need help you.

180 **GHOST.** [*Beneath.*] Swear.

HAM. Rest, rest, perturbéd spirit! So, gentlemen,
With all my love I do commend me to you,
And what so poor a man as Hamlet is
May do t'express his love and friending to you,
185 God willing, shall not lack. Let us go in together,
And still your fingers on your lips, I pray.
The time is out of joint. O curséd spite
That ever I was born to set it right!
Nay, come, let's go together.

[*Exeunt.*]

---

162 **pioneer** miner
171 **antic** mad
173 **encumbered** folded

Act 2

Scene 1

[*Enter old* POLONIUS, *with his man* REYNALDO.]

POL. Give him this money and these notes, Reynaldo.

REY. I will, my lord.

POL. You shall do marvellous wisely, good Reynaldo,
Before you visit him, to make inquire
5   Of his behavior.

REY.   My lord, I did intend it.

POL. Marry, well said, very well said. Look you, sir,
Enquire me first what Danskers° are in Paris,
And how, and who, what means,° and where they keep,
What company, at what expense; and finding
10   By this encompassment° and drift of question
That they do know my son, come you more nearer
Than your particular demands will touch it.
Take you as 'twere some distant knowledge of him,
As thus, 'I know his father and his friends,
15   And in part him'. Do you mark this, Reynaldo?

REY. Ay, very well, my lord.

POL. 'And in part him, but', you may say, 'not well,
But if't be he I mean, he's very wild,
Addicted so and so'. And there put on him
20   What forgeries° you please; marry, none so rank
As may dishonour him. Take heed of that.

---

7   **Danskers** Danes
8   **means** wealth
10   **encompassment** talking round the matter
20   **forgeries** invented wrongdoings

But, sir, such wanton, wild, and usual slips
As are companions noted and most known
To youth and liberty.°

REY.   As gaming, my lord?

25 POL. Ay, or drinking, fencing, swearing, quarrelling,
Drabbing°—you may go so far.

REY. My lord, that would dishonour him.

POL. Faith, no, as you may season° it in the charge.
You must not put another scandal on him,
30   That he is open to incontinency.
That's not my meaning. But breathe his faults so quaintly°
That they may seem the taints of liberty,
The flash and outbreak of a fiery mind,
A savageness in unreclaiméd° blood,
35   Of general assault.°

REY.   But, my good lord—

POL. Wherefore should you do this?

REY.   Ay, my lord,
I would know that.

POL.   Marry, sir, here's my drift,
And I believe it is a fetch of warrant.°
You laying these slight sallies on my son,
40   As 'twere a thing a little soiled i' th' working,
Mark you,
Your party in converse, him you would sound,
Having ever seen in the prenominate° crimes
The youth you breathe of guilty, be assured
45   He closes° with you in this consequence,°
'Good sir', or so, or 'friend', or 'gentleman',

---

24   **liberty** license
26   **Drabbing** whoring
28   **season** moderate
31   **quaintly** delicately
34   **unreclaimed** untamed
35   **Of general assault** assailing all
38   **fetch of warrant** allowable device
43   **prenominate** before-named
45   **closes** agrees
     in this consequence as follows

According to the phrase or the addition°
Of man and country.

REY.   Very good, my lord.

POL.   And then, sir, does 'a this—'a does—What was I about to
say?
50   By the mass, I was about to say something.
Where did I leave?

REY.   At 'closes in the consequence'.

POL.   At 'closes in the consequence'—ay, marry,
He closes thus: 'I know the gentleman.
55   I saw him yesterday, or th' other day,
Or then, or then, with such, or such, and as you say,
There was 'a gaming, there o'ertook in's rouse,
There falling out at tennis', or perchance
'I saw him enter such a house of sale',
60   Videlicet,° a brothel, or so forth.
See you, now—
Your bait of falsehood takes this carp of truth,
And thus do we of wisdom and of reach,°
With windlasses° and with assays of bias,°
65   By indirections find directions out;
So by my former lecture and advice
Shall you my son. You have me, have you not?

REY.   My lord, I have.

POL.   God buy ye;° fare ye well.

REY.   Good my lord.

70   **POL.**   Observe his inclination in yourself.

REY.   I shall, my lord.

POL.   And let him ply his music.

REY.   Well, my lord.

POL.   Farewell.

---

47   **addition** title
60   **Videlicet** namely
63   **reach** ability
64   **windlasses** roundabout approaches
     assays of bias indirect attempts
68   **God buy ye** God be with you

[*Exit* REYNALDO.]

[*Enter* OPHELIA.]

How now, Ophelia, what's the matter?

OPH. O my lord, my lord, I have been so affrighted!

75 POL. With what, i' th' name of God?

OPH. My lord, as I was sewing in my closet,°
Lord Hamlet with his doublet all unbraced,°
No hat upon his head, his stockings fouled,
Ungartered and down-gyvéd° to his ankle,
80 Pale as his shirt, his knees knocking each other,
And with a look so piteous in purport
As if he had been looséd out of hell
To speak of horrors—he comes before me.

POL. Mad for thy love?

OPH. My lord, I do not know,
85 But truly I do fear it.

POL. What said he?

OPH. He took me by the wrist, and held me hard,
Then goes he to the length of all his arm,
And with his other hand thus o'er his brow,
He falls to such perusal of my face
90 As 'a would draw it. Long stayed he so.
At last, a little shaking of mine arm,
And thrice his head thus waving up and down,
He raised a sigh so piteous and profound
As it did seem to shatter all his bulk,
95 And end his being. That done, he lets me go,
And with his head over his shoulder turned
He seemed to find his way without his eyes,
For out adoors he went without their helps,
And to the last bended their light on me.

100 POL. Come, go with me. I will go seek the king.
This is the very ecstasy° of love,

---

76   **closet** private room
77   **unbraced** unlaced
79   **down-gyved** hanging down, like gyves or fetters on a prisoner's ankles
101 **ecstasy** madness

Whose violent property fordoes° itself,
And leads the will to desperate undertakings
As oft as any passion under heaven
105   That does afflict our natures. I am sorry.
What, have you given him any hard words of late?

OPH.   No, my good lord, but as you did command
I did repel his letters, and denied
His access to me.

POL.   That hath made him mad.
110   I am sorry that with better heed and judgment
I had not quoted° him. I feared he did but trifle,
And meant to wrack° thee; but beshrew my jealousy.
By heaven, it is as proper to° our age
To cast beyond ourselves in our opinions
115   As it is common for the younger sort
To lack discretion. Come, go we to the king.
This must be known, which being kept close,° might move°
More grief to hide than hate to utter love.
Come.

[*Exeunt.*]

Scene 2

[*Flourish. Enter* KING *and* QUEEN, ROSENCRANTZ *and* GUILDENSTERN, *and* ATTENDANTS.]

KING.   Welcome, dear Rosencrantz and Guildenstern.
Moreover that we much did long to see you,
The need we have to use you did provoke
Our hasty sending. Something have you heard
5   Of Hamlet's transformation—so call it,
Sith° nor th' exterior nor the inward man
Resembles that it was. What it should be,

102	**fordoes**	destroys
111	**quoted**	observed
112	**wrack**	ruin
113	**proper to**	characteristic of
117	**close**	secret
	move	cause
6	**Sith**	since

More than his father's death, that thus hath put him
So much from th' understanding of himself,
10   I cannot dream of. I entreat you both
That, being of so young days brought up with him,
And sith so neighboured to his youth and havior,
That you vouchsafe your rest here in our court
Some little time, so by your companies
15   To draw him on to pleasures, and to gather
So much as from occasion you may glean,
Whether aught to us unknown afflicts him thus,
That opened° lies within our remedy.

QUEEN. Good gentlemen, he hath much talked of you,
20   And sure I am two men there is not living
To whom he more adheres. If it will please you
To show us so much gentry° and good will
As to expend your time with us awhile
For the supply and profit of our hope,
25   Your visitation shall receive such thanks
As fits a king's remembrance.

ROS.   Both your majesties
Might, by the sovereign power you have of us,
Put your dread pleasures more into command
Than to entreaty.

GUIL.   But we both obey,
30   And here give up ourselves in the full bent
To lay our service freely at your feet,
To be commanded.

KING. Thanks, Rosencrantz and gentle Guildenstern.

QUEEN. Thanks, Guildenstern and gentle Rosencrantz.
35   And I beseech you instantly to visit
My too much changed son. Go, some of you,
And bring these gentlemen where Hamlet is.

GUIL. Heavens make our presence and our practices
Pleasant and helpful to him!

QUEEN.   Ay, amen!

[Exeunt ROSENCRANTZ and GUILDENSTERN with some ATTENDANTS.]

---

18   **opened** disclosed
22   **gentry** courtesy

[Enter POLONIUS.]

40   **POL.** Th' ambassadors from Norway, my good lord,
        Are joyfully returned.

      KING. Thou still° hast been the father of good news.

      POL. Have I, my lord? I assure my good liege,
        I hold my duty as I hold my soul,
45   Both to my God and to my gracious king;
        And I do think—or else this brain of mine
        Hunts not the trail of policy so sure
        As it hath used to do—that I have found
        The very cause of Hamlet's lunacy.

50   **KING.** O, speak of that, that do I long to hear.

      POL. Give first admittance to th' ambassadors.
        My news shall be the fruit to that great feast.

      KING. Thyself do grace to them, and bring them in.

[Exit POLONIUS.]

      He tells me, my dear Gertrude, he hath found
55   The head and source of all your son's distemper.

      QUEEN. I doubt° it is no other but the main,
        His father's death and our o'erhasty marriage.

      KING. Well, we shall sift him.

[Enter Ambassadors VOLTEMAND *and* CORNELIUS, *with* POLONIUS.]

                           Welcome, my good friends,
      Say, Voltemand, what from our brother Norway?

60   **VOL.** Most fair return of greetings and desires.
        Upon our first, he sent out to suppress
        His nephew's levies, which to him appeared
        To be a preparation 'gainst the Polack,°
        But better looked into, he truly found
65   It was against your highness, whereat grieved,
        That so his sickness, age, and impotence
        Was falsely borne in hand,° sends out arrests

---

42   **still** ever
56   **doubt** suspect
63   **the Polack** the Polish nation
67   **borne in hand** deceived

On Fortinbras, which he in brief obeys,
Receives rebuke from Norway, and in fine,°
70 Makes vow before his uncle never more
To give th' assay° of arms against your majesty.
Whereon old Norway, overcome with joy,
Gives him threescore thousand crowns in annual fee,
And his commission to employ those soldiers,
75 So levied as before, against the Polack,
With an entreaty, herein further shown, [*Gives a paper.*]
That it might please you to give quiet pass
Through your dominions for this enterprise,
On such regards° of safety and allowance
80 As therein are set down.

KING.   It likes us well,
And at our more considered time we'll read,
Answer, and think upon this business.
Meantime we thank you for your well-took labor.
Go to your rest; at night we'll feast together.
85 Most welcome home!

[*Exeunt* AMBASSADORS.]

POL.   This business is well ended.
My liege and madam, to expostulate
What majesty should be, what duty is,
Why day is day, night night, and time is time,
Were nothing but to waste night, day, and time.
90 Therefore, since brevity is the soul of wit,°
And tediousness the limbs and outward flourishes,
I will be brief. Your noble son is mad.
Mad call I it, for to define true madness,
What is't but to be nothing else but mad?
95 But let that go.

QUEEN.   More matter° with less art.

POL. Madam, I swear I use no art at all.
That he is mad, 'tis true: 'tis true 'tis pity,

---

69 **in fine** in the end
71 **assay** trial
79 **regards** considerations
90 **wit** understanding
95 **matter** meaning, sense

And pity 'tis 'tis true. A foolish figure,
But farewell it, for I will use no art.
100 Mad let us grant him, then, and now remains
That we find out the cause of this effect,
Or rather say the cause of this defect,
For this effect defective comes by cause.
Thus it remains, and the remainder thus.
105 Perpend.°
I have a daughter—have while she is mine—
Who in her duty and obedience, mark,
Hath given me this. Now gather, and surmise. [*Reads.*]
 'To the celestial, and my soul's idol, the most beautified
110 Ophelia.'—That's an ill phrase, a vile phrase, 'beautified' is a
vile phrase. But you shall hear. Thus: [*Reads.*]
 'In her excellent white bosom, these, etc.'

QUEEN. Came this from Hamlet to her?

POL. Good madam, stay awhile. I will be faithful.

[*Reads Letter.*]

115   'Doubt thou the stars are fire,
         Doubt that the sun doth move;
         Doubt truth to be a liar;
         But never doubt I love.

O dear Ophelia, I am ill at these numbers.° I have not art
120 to reckon my groans, but that I love thee best, O most best, believe it. Adieu.
                    Thine evermore, most dear lady, whilst
                        this machine° is to him, HAMLET.'
This in obedience hath my daughter shown me,
125 And more above, hath his solicitings,
As they fell out by time, by means, and place,
All given to mine ear.

KING.   But how hath she
Received his love?

POL.   What do you think of me?

KING. As of a man faithful and honorable.

---

105   **Perpend** consider
119   **numbers** verses
123   **machine** body

130 **POL.** I would fain prove so. But what might you think,
When I had seen this hot love on the wing,
(As I perceived it, I must tell you that,
Before my daughter told me), what might you,
Or my dear majesty your queen here, think,
135 If I had played the desk or table-book,°
Or given my heart a winking, mute and dumb,
Or looked upon this love with idle sight,
What might you think? No, I went round° to work,
And my young mistress thus I did bespeak:
140 'Lord Hamlet is a prince out of thy star.
This must not be'. And then I prescripts gave her,
That she should lock herself from his resort,
Admit no messengers, receive no tokens.
Which done, she took the fruits of my advice;
145 And he repelled, a short tale to make,
Fell into a sadness, then into a fast,
Thence to a watch,° thence into a weakness,
Thence to a lightness,° and by this declension,
Into the madness wherein now he raves,
150 And all we mourn for.

KING.   Do you think 'tis this?

QUEEN. It may be, very like.

POL. Hath there been such a time—I would fain know that—
That I have positively said ''Tis so',
When it proved otherwise?

KING.   Not that I know.

POL. [*Pointing to his head and shoulder.*] Take this from this,
155   if this be otherwise.
If circumstances lead me, I will find
Where truth is hid, though it were hid indeed
Within the centre.°

KING.   How may we try it further?

POL. You know sometimes he walks four hours together

---

135   **played . . . table-book** acted as silent go-between
138   **round** directly
147   **watch** sleeplessness
148   **lightness** lightheadedness
158   **centre** centre of the earth and of the Ptolemaic universe

160   Here in the lobby.

QUEEN.   So he does, indeed.

POL. At such a time I'll loose my daughter to him.
Be you and I behind an arras then.
Mark the encounter. If he love her not,
And be not from his reason fall'n thereon,
165   Let me be no assistant for a state,
But keep a farm and carters.

KING.   We will try it.

[*Enter* HAMLET *reading on a book.*]

QUEEN. But look where sadly the poor wretch comes reading.

POL. Away, I do beseech you both away,
I'll board° him presently.°

[*Exeunt* KING *and* QUEEN *with* ATTENDANTS.]

                    O, give me leave,
170   How does my good Lord Hamlet?

HAM. Well, God-a-mercy.

POL. Do you know me, my lord?

HAM. Excellent well, you are a fishmonger.

POL. Not I, my lord.

175   **HAM.** Then I would you were so honest a man.

POL. Honest, my lord?

HAM. Ay, sir, to be honest as this world goes, is to be one man picked out of ten thousand.

POL. That's very true, my lord.

180   **HAM.** For if the sun breed maggots in a dead dog, being a good kissing carrion—Have you a daughter?

POL. I have, my lord.

HAM. Let her not walk i' th' sun. Conception is a blessing, but as your daughter may conceive—friend, look to't.

185   **POL.** [*Aside.*] How say you by that? Still harping on my daughter. Yet he knew me not at first. 'A said I was a fishmonger. 'A is far gone. And truly in my youth I suffered much extremity for love,

---

   169   **board** accost
           presently immediately

very near this. I'll speak to him again.—What do you read, my lord?

190 HAM. Words, words, words.

POL. What is the matter, my lord?

HAM. Between who?

POL. I mean the matter that you read, my lord.

HAM. Slanders, sir; for the satirical rogue says here that old men
195 have grey beards, that their faces are wrinkled, their eyes purging thick amber and plum-tree gum, and that they have a plentiful lack of wit, together with most weak hams—all which, sir, though I most powerfully and potently believe, yet I hold it not honesty to have it thus set down, for yourself, sir, shall grow old as I am, if
200 like a crab you could go backward.

POL. [Aside.] Though this be madness, yet there is method in't.—
Will you walk out of the air, my lord?

HAM. Into my grave?

POL. [Aside.] Indeed, that's out of the air. How pregnant° sometimes
205 his replies are! a happiness° that often madness hits on, which reason and sanity could not so prosperously be delivered of. I will leave him, and suddenly contrive the means of meeting between him and my daughter.—My lord, I will take my leave of you.

HAM. You cannot take from me anything that I will not more
210 willingly part withal—except my life, except my life, except my life.

[Enter GUILDENSTERN and ROSENCRANTZ.]

POL. Fare you well, my lord.

HAM. These tedious old fools!

POL. You go to seek the Lord Hamlet. There he is.

215 ROS. [To POLONIUS.] God save you, sir!

[Exit POLONIUS.]

GUIL. My honored lord!

ROS. My most dear lord!

HAM. My excellent good friends! How dost thou, Guildenstern? Ah, Rosencrantz! Good lads, how do you both?

---

204 **pregnant** full of meaning
205 **happiness** aptness

220   **ROS.** As the indifferent° children of the earth.

  GUIL. Happy in that we are not over-happy;
    On Fortune's cap we are not the very button.°

  HAM. Nor the soles of her shoe?

  ROS. Neither, my lord.

225   **HAM.** Then you live about her waist, or in the middle of her favors.

  GUIL. Faith, her privates we.

  HAM. In the secret parts of Fortune? O, most true, she is a strumpet. What news?

230   **ROS.** None, my lord, but that the world's grown honest.

  HAM. Then is doomsday near. But your news is not true. Let me question more in particular. What have you, my good friends, deserved at the hands of Fortune, that she sends you to prison hither?

235   **GUIL.** Prison, my lord?

  HAM. Denmark's a prison.

  ROS. Then is the world one.

  HAM. A goodly one, in which there are many confines, wards, and dungeons, Denmark being one o' th' worst.

240   **ROS.** We think not so, my lord.

  HAM. Why then 'tis none to you; for there is nothing either good or bad, but thinking makes it so. To me it is a prison.

  ROS. Why then your ambition makes it one. 'Tis too narrow for your mind.

245   **HAM.** O God, I could be bounded in a nutshell and count myself a king of infinite space, were it not that I have bad dreams.

  GUIL. Which dreams indeed are ambition; for the very substance of the ambitious is merely the shadow of a dream.

  HAM. A dream itself is but a shadow.

250   **ROS.** Truly, and I hold ambition of so airy and light a quality that it is but a shadow's shadow.

---

220   **indifferent** average
222   **button** knob on the top of a cap

HAM. Then are our beggars bodies, and our monarchs and out-
stretched heroes the beggars' shadows. Shall we to th' court? for,
by my fay,° I cannot reason.

255 **BOTH.** We'll wait upon you.

HAM. No such matter. I will not sort you with° the rest of my servants;
for to speak to you like an honest man, I am most dreadfully
attended. But in the beaten way of friendship, what make you at
Elsinore?

260 **ROS.** To visit you, my lord; no other occasion.

HAM. Beggar that I am, I am even poor in thanks, but I thank you;
and sure, dear friends, my thanks are too dear a halfpenny. Were
you not sent for? Is it your own inclining? Is it a free visitation?
Come, come, deal justly with me. Come, come, nay speak.

265 **GUIL.** What should we say, my lord?

HAM. Anything but to th' purpose. You were sent for, and there is a
kind of confession in your looks, which your modesties have not
craft enough to color. I know the good king and queen have sent
for you.

270 **ROS.** To what end, my lord?

HAM. That you must teach me. But let me conjure you by the rights
of our fellowship, by the consonancy of our youth, by the
obligation of our ever-preserved love, and by what more dear a
better proposer can charge you withal, be even and direct with me
275 whether you were sent for or no.

ROS. [*Aside to GUILDENSTERN.*] What say you?

HAM. [*Aside.*] Nay, then, I have an eye of you.—If you love me,
hold not off.

GUIL. My lord, we were sent for.

280 **HAM.** I will tell you why; so shall my anticipation prevent° your
discovery,° and your secrecy to the king and queen moult no feather.
I have of late—but wherefore I know not—lost all my mirth, for-
gone all custom of exercises; and indeed it goes so heavily with my

---

254 **fay** faith
256 **sort you with** put you in the same class with
280 **prevent** forestall
281 **discovery** disclosure

285 disposition, that this goodly frame the earth seems to me a sterile promontory, this most excellent canopy the air, look you, this brave o'er-hanging firmament, this majestical roof fretted° with golden fire, why it appeareth nothing to me but a foul and pestilent congregation of vapors. What a piece of work is a man, how noble in reason, how infinite in faculties, in form and moving, how express 290 and admirable in action, how like an angel in apprehension, how like a god: the beauty of the world, the paragon of animals. And yet to me, what is this quintessence of dust? Man delights not me, nor woman neither, though by your smiling you seem to say so.

ROS. My lord, there was no such stuff in my thoughts.

295 HAM. Why did ye laugh, then, when I said 'Man delights not me'?

ROS. To think, my lord, if you delight not in man, what lenten° entertainment the players shall receive from you. We coted° them on the way, and hither are they coming to offer you service.

300 HAM. He that plays the king shall be welcome—his majesty shall have tribute on me; the adventurous knight shall use his foil and target;° the lover shall not sigh gratis; the humorous man° shall end his part in peace; the clown shall make those laugh whose lungs are tickle o' th' sere;° and the lady shall say her mind freely, or the 305 blank verse shall halt° for't. What players are they?

ROS. Even those you were wont to take such delight in, the tragedians of the city.

HAM. How chances it they travel? Their residence, both in reputation and profit, was better both ways.

---

286 **fretted** decorated with fretwork
297 **lenten** scanty
298 **coted** passed
301–302 **foil and target** spear and shield
302 **humorous man** the actor who plays the eccentric character dominated by one of the four humors
304 **tickle o' th' sere** easily set off (*sere* is that part of a gunlock which keeps the hammer at full or half cock)
305 **halt** limp

310 ROS. I think their inhibition° comes by the means of the late
     innovation.°

HAM. Do they hold the same estimation they did when I was in the
     city? Are they so followed?

ROS. No, indeed, are they not.

315 HAM. How comes it? Do they grow rusty?

ROS. Nay, their endeavor keeps in the wonted pace; but there
     is, sir, an eyrie° of children, little eyases,° that cry out on the top of
     question,° and are most tyrannically clapped for't. These are now
     the fashion, and so berattle the common stages° (so they call them)
320 that many wearing rapiers are afraid of goose quills° and dare
     scarce come thither.

HAM. What, are they children? Who maintains 'em? How are
     they escoted?° Will they pursue the quality° no longer than they can
     sing?° Will they not say afterwards, if they should grow themselves
325 to common players (as it is most like, if their means are no better),
     their writers do them wrong to make them exclaim against their
     own succession?

ROS. Faith, there has been much to do on both sides; and the na-
     tion holds it no sin to tarre° them to controversy. There was for a
330 while no money bid for argument,° unless the poet and the
     player went to cuffs in the question.

---

    310   **inhibition** prohibition of plays by authority (possibly with reference to decree of the Privy
           Council of 22 June 1600, limiting the number of London theater companies to two, and stipu-
           lating that the two were to perform only twice a week)
    311   **innovation** meaning uncertain (sometimes taken to refer to the re-introduction, ca. 1600,
           on the London theatrical scene of companies of boy actors performing in private theaters;
           sometimes interpreted as "political upheaval," wth special reference to Essex's rebellion,
           February, 1601)
    317   **eyrie** nest
           eyases nestling hawks (here, the boys in the children's companies training as actors)
317–318   **on the top of question** louder than all others on matter of dispute
    319   **common stages** public theaters of the **common players** (below, line 325), organized in
           companies composed mainly of adult actors
    320   **goose quills** pens (of the satiric dramatists writing for the private theaters)
    323   **escoted** maintained
           pursue the quality continue in the profession of acting
    324   **sing** i.e., until their voices change
    329   **tarre** incite
    330   **argument** plot of a play

HAM. Is't possible?

GUIL. O, there has been much throwing about of brains.

HAM. Do the boys carry it away?

335 **ROS.** Ay, that they do, my lord, Hercules and his load° too.

HAM. It is not very strange, for my uncle is King of Denmark, and
those that would make mouths° at him while my father lived give
twenty, forty, fifty, a hundred ducats apiece for his picture in little.°
'Sblood, there is something in this more than natural, if philoso-
340 phy could find it out.

[*A flourish.*]

GUIL. There are the players.

HAM. Gentlemen, you are welcome to Elsinore. Your hands. Come
then, th' appurtenance° of welcome is fashion and ceremony.
Let me comply with you in this garb, lest my extent° to the play-
345 ers, which I tell you must show fairly outwards, should more appear like entertainment than yours. You are welcome. But my
uncle-father and aunt-mother are deceived.

GUIL. In what, my dear lord?

HAM. I am but mad north-north-west; when the wind is southerly
350 I know a hawk° from a handsaw.°

[*Enter POLONIUS.*]

POL. Well be with you, gentlemen.

HAM. Hark you, Guildenstern—and you too—at each ear a hearer.
That great baby you see there is not yet out of his swaddling clouts.

ROS. Happily° he is the second time come to them, for they say an
355 old man is twice a child.

---

335   **load** i.e., the world (the sign of the Globe Theatre represented Hercules bearing the world on
his shoulders)

337   **mouths** grimaces

338   **in little** in miniature

343   **appurtenance** adjuncts

344   **extent** welcome

350   **hawk** mattock or pickaxe (also called "hack," here used with a play on *hawk* as a bird)
handsaw a saw managed with one hand (here used with a play on some corrupt form of
hernshaw, "heron")

354   **Happily** perhaps

HAM. I will prophesy he comes to tell me of the players. Mark it.
—You say right, sir, a Monday morning, 'twas then indeed.

POL. My lord, I have news to tell you.

HAM. My lord, I have news to tell you.
360   When Roscius° was an actor in Rome—

POL. The actors are come hither, my lord.

HAM. Buzz, buzz.

POL. Upon my honor—

HAM. Then came each actor on his ass—

365 **POL.** The best actors in the world, either for tragedy, comedy, history, pastoral, pastoral-comical, historical-pastoral, tragical-historical, tragical-comical-historical-pastoral, scene individable,° or poem unlimited.° Seneca° cannot be too heavy nor Plautus° too light. For the law of writ and the liberty,° these are the only men.

370 **HAM.** O Jephthah,° judge of Israel, what a treasure hadst thou!

POL. What a treasure had he, my lord?

HAM. Why—

> 'One fair daughter, and no more,
> The which he loved passing well'.

375 **POL.** [*Aside*.] Still on my daughter.

HAM. Am I not i' th' right, old Jephthah?

POL. If you call me Jephthah, my lord, I have a daughter that I love passing well.

HAM. Nay, that follows not.

380 **POL.** What follows then, my lord?

---

360 **Roscius** the greatest of Roman comic actors, though regarded by the Elizabethans as a tragic one

367 **scene individable** i.e., a play that observes the unities of time and place

368 **poem unlimited** a play that does not observe the unities
      Seneca Roman writer of tragedies
      Plautus Roman comic dramatist

369 **law of writ and the liberty** i.e., plays according to strict classical rules, and those that ignored the unities of time and place

370 **Jephthah** was compelled to sacrifice a beloved daughter (Judges 11). Hamlet quotes from a contemporary ballad titled *Jephthah, Judge of Israel* at lines 373–74, 382, and 384.

HAM. Why—

'As by lot, God wot'

and then, you know,

'It came to pass, as most like it was.'

385   The first row° of the pious chanson will show you more, for look
where my abridgement comes.

[*Enter the* PLAYERS.]

You are welcome, masters; welcome, all.—I am glad to see thee
well.—Welcome, good friends.—O, old friend! Why thy face is
valanced° since I saw thee last. Com'st thou to beard me in Den-
390   mark?—What, my young lady° and mistress? By'r lady, your lady-
ship is nearer to heaven than when I saw you last by the altitude
of a chopine.° Pray God your voice, like a piece of uncurrent gold,
be not cracked within the ring.°—Masters, you are all welcome.
We'll e'en to't like French falconers, fly at anything we see. We'll
395   have a speech straight.° Come give us a taste of your quality, come
a passionate speech.

1 PLAY. What speech, my good lord?

HAM. I heard thee speak me a speech once, but it was never
acted, or if it was, not above once, for the play, I remember, pleased
400   not the million; 'twas caviary° to the general.° But it was—as I received it, and others whose judgments in such matters cried in the
top of mine—an excellent play, well digested° in the scenes, set
down with as much modesty as cunning. I remember one said
there were no sallets° in the lines to make the matter savory, nor no
405   matter in the phrase that might indict the author of affectation, but
called it an honest method, as wholesome as sweet, and by very

---

385	**row** stanza	
389	**valanced** bearded	
390	**young lady** i.e., the boy who plays female roles	
392	**chopine** a shoe with high cork heel and sole	
393	**cracked within the ring** a coin cracked within the circle surrounding the head of the sovereign was no longer legal tender and so *uncurrent*	
395	**straight** immediately	
400	**caviary** caviare	
	general multitude	
402	**digested** arranged	
404	**sallets** salads, highly seasoned passages	

much more handsome than fine.° One speech in't I chiefly loved.
'Twas Æneas' tale to Dido, and thereabout of it especially when
he speaks of Priam's slaughter. If it live in your memory, begin at
410 this line—let me see, let me see:

> 'The rugged Pyrrhus, like th' Hyrcanian beast'°—

'tis not so; it begins with Pyrrhus—

> 'The rugged Pyrrhus, he whose sable arms,
> Black as his purpose, did the night resemble
415 When he lay couchéd in th' ominous horse,°
> Hath now this dread and black complexion smeared
> With heraldry more dismal; head to foot
> Now is he total gules,° horridly tricked°
> With blood of fathers, mothers, daughters, sons,
420 Baked and impasted with the parching streets,
> That lend a tyrannous and a damnéd light
> To their lord's murder. Roasted in wrath and fire,
> And thus o'er-sizéd° with coagulate° gore,
> With eyes like carbuncles, the hellish Pyrrhus
425 Old grandsire Priam seeks.'

So proceed you.

POL. Fore God, my lord, well spoken, with good accent and good
discretion.

1 PLAY.   'Anon he finds him
430 Striking too short at Greeks. His antique sword,
Rebellious to his arm, lies where it falls,
Repugnant° to command. Unequal matched,
Pyrrhus at Priam drives, in rage strikes wide.
But with the whiff and wind of his fell° sword
435 Th' unnervéd father falls. Then senseless Ilium,
Seeming to feel this blow, with flaming top

---

407   **more handsome than fine** admirable rather than appealing by mere cleverness
411   **Hyrcanian beast** tiger
415   **horse** i.e., the Trojan horse
418   **gules** heraldic term for red
      tricked delineated
423   **o'er-sized** covered as with size
      coagulate clotted
432   **Repugnant** refractory
434   **fell** fierce, cruel

Stoops to his base, and with a hideous crash
Takes prisoner Pyrrhus' ear. For, lo! his sword,
Which was declining on the milky head
440   Of reverend Priam, seemed i' th' air to stick.
So as a painted tyrant Pyrrhus stood,
And like a neutral to his will and matter,
Did nothing.
But as we often see, against° some storm,
445   A silence in the heavens, the rack° stand still,
The bold winds speechless, and the orb below
As hush as death, anon the dreadful thunder
Doth rend the region;° so, after Pyrrhus' pause,
A rouséd vengeance sets him new awork,
450   And never did the Cyclops'° hammers fall
On Mars's armor, forged for proof eterne,°
With less remorse than Pyrrhus' bleeding sword
Now falls on Priam.
Out, out, thou strumpet, Fortune! All you gods,
455   In general synod take away her power,
Break all the spokes and fellies° from her wheel,
And bowl the round nave° down the hill of heaven
As low as to the fiends.'

POL. This is too long.

460   HAM. It shall to the barber's with your beard.—Prithee say on.
He's for a jig, or a tale of bawdry, or he sleeps. Say on; come to
Hecuba.

1 PLAY. 'But who, ah woe! had seen the mobled° queen—'

HAM. 'The mobled queen'?

465   POL. That's good.

1 PLAY. 'Run barefoot up and down, threat'ning the flames

---

444   **against** just before
445   **rack** mass of cloud
448   **region** air
450   **Cyclops** giant workmen who made armor in the smithy of Vulcan
451   **proof eterne** to be forever impenetrable
456   **fellies** the curved pieces forming the rim of a wheel
457   **nave** hub of a wheel
463   **mobled** muffled
467   **bisson rheum** blinding tears

With bisson rheum,° a clout upon that head
Where late the diadem stood, and for a robe,
About her lank and all o'er-teeméd° loins,
470   A blanket, in the alarm of fear caught up—
Who this had seen, with tongue in venom steeped,
'Gainst Fortune's state° would treason have pronounced.
But if the gods themselves did see her then,
When she saw Pyrrhus make malicious sport
475   In mincing with his sword her husband's limbs,
The instant burst of clamor that she made,
Unless things mortal move them not at all,
Would have made milch° the burning eyes of heaven,
And passion in the gods.'

480   **POL.** Look whe'r he has not turned his color, and has tears in's eyes.
Prithee no more.

HAM. 'Tis well. I'll have thee speak out the rest of this soon.—
Good my lord, will you see the players well bestowed? Do you
hear, let them be well used, for they are the abstract° and brief
485   chronicles of the time; after your death you were better have a bad
epitaph than their ill report while you live.

POL. My lord, I will use them according to their desert.

HAM. God's bodkin,° man, much better. Use every man after his
desert, and who shall 'scape whipping? Use them after your own
490   honor and dignity. The less they deserve, the more merit is in your
bounty. Take them in.

POL. Come, sirs.

HAM. Follow him, friends. We'll hear a play tomorrow. [*Aside to
First Player.*] Dost thou hear me, old friend, can you play 'The
495   Murder of Gonzago'?

1 PLAY. Ay, my lord.

HAM. We'll ha't tomorrow night. You could for a need study a speech
of some dozen or sixteen lines which I would set down and insert
in't, could you not?

---

469   **o'er-teemed** exhausted by many births
472   **state** government
478   **milch** moist, tearful (lit., milk-giving)
484   **abstract** summary account
488   **God's bodkin** by God's dear body

500   1 PLAY. Ay, my lord.

       HAM. Very well. Follow that lord, and look you mock him not.

[*Exeunt* POLONIUS *and* PLAYERS.]

       My good friends, I'll leave you till night. You are welcome to
       Elsinore.

       ROS. Good my lord.

[*Exeunt* ROSENCRANTZ *and* GUILDENSTERN.]

505   HAM. Ay, so God buy to you. Now I am alone.
              O, what a rogue and peasant slave am I!
              Is it not monstrous that this player here,
              But in a fiction, in a dream of passion,
              Could force his soul so to his own conceit°
510   That from her working all his visage wanned;
              Tears in his eyes, distraction in his aspect,
              A broken voice, and his whole function suiting
              With forms to his conceit? And all for nothing,
515   For Hecuba!
              What's Hecuba to him or he to her,
              That he should weep for her? What would he do
              Had he the motive and the cue for passion
              That I have? He would drown the stage with tears,
              And cleave the general° ear with horrid speech,
520   Make mad the guilty, and appal the free,
              Confound the ignorant, and amaze indeed
              The very faculties of eyes and ears.
              Yet I,
              A dull and muddy-mettled° rascal, peak°
525   Like John-a-dreams, unpregnant° of my cause,
              And can say nothing; no, not for a king
              Upon whose property and most dear life
              A damned defeat was made. Am I a coward?

---

509   **conceit** imagination
519   **general** public
524   **muddy-mettled** dull-spirited
       peak mope
525   **unpregnant** not quickened to action

Who calls me villain, breaks my pate across,
530 Plucks off my beard and blows it in my face,
Tweaks me by the nose, gives me the lie i' th' throat
As deep as to the lungs? Who does me this?
Ha, 'swounds, I should take it; for it cannot be
But I am pigeon-livered and lack gall
535 To make oppression bitter, or ere this
I should 'a fatted all the region kites°
With this slave's offal. Bloody, bawdy villain!
Remorseless, treacherous, lecherous, kindless° villain!
Why, what an ass am I! This is most brave,
540 That I, the son of a dear father murdered,
Prompted to my revenge by heaven and hell,
Must like a whore unpack my heart with words,
And fall a-cursing like a very drab,
A scullion!° Fie upon't! foh!
545 About, my brains. Hum—I have heard
That guilty creatures sitting at a play,
Have by the very cunning of the scene
Been struck so to the soul that presently°
They have proclaimed their malefactions;
550 For murder, though it have no tongue, will speak
With most miraculous organ. I'll have these players
Play something like the murder of my father
Before mine uncle. I'll observe his looks.
I'll tent° him to the quick. If 'a do blench,°
555 I know my course. The spirit that I have seen
May be a devil, and the devil hath power

---

536 **region kites** kites of the air
538 **kindless** unnatural
544 **scullion** kitchen wench
548 **presently** immediately
554 **tent** probe
blench flinch

T' assume a pleasing shape, yea, and perhaps
Out of my weakness and my melancholy,
As he is very potent with such spirits,
560   Abuses° me to damn me. I'll have grounds
More relative° than this. The play's the thing
Wherein I'll catch the conscience of the king.

[*Exit.*]

---

560   **Abuses** deludes
561   **relative** relevant

Act 3

Scene 1

[*Enter* KING, QUEEN, POLONIUS, OPHELIA, ROSENCRANTZ, GUILDENSTERN, LORDS.]

KING. And can you by no drift of conference
Get from him why he puts on this confusion,
Grating so harshly all his days of quiet
With turbulent and dangerous lunacy?

5 ROS. He does confess he feels himself distracted,
But from what cause 'a will by no means speak.

GUIL. Nor do we find him forward° to be sounded,
But with crafty madness keeps aloof
When we would bring him on to some confession
10   Of his true state.

QUEEN.   Did he receive you well?

ROS. Most like a gentleman.

GUIL. But with much forcing of his disposition.

ROS. Niggard of question, but of our demands
Most free in his reply.

QUEEN.   Did you assay° him
15   To any pastime?

ROS. Madam, it so fell out that certain players
We o'er-raught° on the way. Of these we told him,
And there did seem in him a kind of joy
To hear of it. They are here about the court,

---

7 **forward** willing
14 **assay** try to win
17 **o'er-raught** overtook

| 20 | And as I think, they have already order |
| | This night to play before him. |

POL.   'Tis most true,
And he beseeched me to entreat your majesties
To hear and see the matter.

KING. With all my heart, and it doth much content me
25   To hear him so inclined.
       Good gentlemen, give him a further edge,°
       And drive his purpose into these delights.

ROS. We shall, my lord.

[*Exeunt* ROSENCRANTZ *and* GUILDENSTERN.]

KING.   Sweet Gertrude, leave us too,
       For we have closely° sent for Hamlet hither,
30   That he, as 'twere by accident, may here
       Affront° Ophelia.
       Her father and myself (lawful espials)°
       We'll so bestow ourselves that, seeing unseen,
       We may of their encounter frankly judge,
35   And gather by him, as he is behaved,
       If't be th' affliction of his love or no
       That thus he suffers for.

QUEEN.   I shall obey you.—
       And for your part, Ophelia, I do wish
       That your good beauties be the happy cause
40   Of Hamlet's wildness. So shall I hope your virtues
       Will bring him to his wonted way again,
       To both your honors.

OPH.   Madam, I wish it may.

[*Exit* QUEEN *with* LORDS.]

POL. Ophelia, walk you here.—Gracious, so please you,
       We will bestow ourselves.—[*To* OPHELIA.] Read on this book,
45   That show of such an exercise° may color°

---

26 **give him a further edge** sharpen his inclination
29 **closely** privately
31 **Affront** meet face to face
32 **espials** spies
45 **exercise** act of devotion
    color give an appearance of naturalness to

Your loneliness.—We are oft to blame in this,
'Tis too much proved, that with devotion's visage
And pious action we do sugar o'er
The devil himself.

KING. [*Aside.*]   O, 'tis too true.
50 How smart a lash that speech doth give my conscience!
The harlot's cheek, beautied with plast'ring art,
Is not more ugly to° the thing that helps it
Than is my deed to my most painted word.
O heavy burden!

55 POL. I hear him coming. Let's withdraw, my lord.

[*Exeunt KING and POLONIUS.*]

[*Enter HAMLET.*]

HAM. To be, or not to be, that is the question:
Whether 'tis nobler in the mind to suffer
The slings and arrows of outrageous fortune,
Or to take arms against a sea of troubles,
60 And by opposing end them. To die, to sleep—
No more; and by a sleep to say we end
The heartache, and the thousand natural shocks
That flesh is heir to: 'tis a consummation
Devoutly to be wished. To die, to sleep—
65 To sleep, perchance to dream, ay there's the rub;°
For in that sleep of death what dreams may come
When we have shuffled off this mortal coil°
Must give us pause. There's the respect
That makes calamity of so long life:
70 For who would bear the whips and scorns of time,
Th' oppressor's wrong, the proud man's contumely,
The pangs of despised love, the law's delay,
The insolence of office, and the spurns
That patient merit of th' unworthy takes,
75 When he himself might his quietus° make
With a bare bodkin?° Who would fardels° bear,

---

52 **to** compared to
65 **rub** obstacle (lit., obstruction encountered by bowler's ball)
67 **coil** bustle, turmoil
75 **quietus** settlement
76 **bodkin** dagger
    fardels burdens

To grunt and sweat under a weary life,
But that the dread of something after death,
The undiscovered country, from whose bourn°
80   No traveller returns, puzzles the will,
And makes us rather bear those ills we have
Than fly to others that we know not of?
Thus conscience does make cowards of us all,
And thus the native hue of resolution
85   Is sicklied o'er with the pale cast of thought,
And enterprises of great pitch° and moment
With this regard° their currents turn awry
And lose the name of action. Soft you now,
The fair Ophelia.—Nymph, in thy orisons°
90   Be all my sins remembered.

    OPH.   Good my lord,
How does your honor for this many a day?

    HAM. I humbly thank you, well.

    OPH. My lord, I have remembrances of yours
That I have longed long to re-deliver.
95   I pray you now receive them.

    HAM.   No, not I,
I never gave you aught.

    OPH. My honored lord, you know right well you did,
And with them words of so sweet breath composed
As made the things more rich. Their perfume lost,
100   Take these again, for to the noble mind
Rich gifts wax poor when givers prove unkind.
There, my lord.

    HAM. Ha, ha! are you honest?°

    OPH. My lord?

105   **HAM.** Are you fair?

    OPH. What means your lordship?

79	**bourn**	realm
86	**pitch**	height
87	**regard**	consideration
89	**orisons**	prayers
103	**honest**	chaste

HAM. That if you be honest and fair, your honesty should admit no discourse to your beauty.

OPH. Could beauty, my lord, have better commerce than with
110   honesty?

HAM. Ay, truly, for the power of beauty will sooner transform honesty from what it is to a bawd than the force of honesty can translate beauty into his likeness. This was sometime a paradox, but now the time gives it proof. I did love you once.

115 **OPH.** Indeed, my lord, you made me believe so.

HAM. You should not have believed me, for virtue cannot so inoculate° our old stock but we shall relish of it. I loved you not.

OPH. I was the more deceived.

HAM. Get thee to a nunnery. Why wouldst thou be a breeder of
120   sinners? I am myself indifferent honest,° but yet I could accuse me of such things that it were better my mother had not borne me: I am very proud, revengeful, ambitious, with more offences at my beck than I have thoughts to put them in, imagination to give them shape, or time to act them in. What should such fellows as
125   I do crawling between earth and heaven? We are arrant knaves all; believe none of us. Go thy ways to a nunnery. Where's your father?

OPH. At home, my lord.

HAM. Let the doors be shut upon him, that he may play the fool
130   nowhere but in's own house. Farewell.

OPH. O, help him, you sweet heavens!

HAM. If thou dost marry, I'll give thee this plague for thy dowry: be thou as chaste as ice, as pure as snow, thou shalt not escape calumny. Get thee to a nunnery, farewell. Or if thou wilt needs
135   marry, marry a fool, for wise men know well enough what monsters you make of them. To a nunnery, go, and quickly too. Farewell.

OPH. Heavenly powers, restore him!

HAM. I have heard of your paintings well enough. God hath given
140   you one face, and you make yourselves another. You jig and

---

117   **inoculate** graft
120   **indifferent honest** moderately respectable

amble, and you lisp; you nickname God's creatures, and make your
wantonness your ignorance.° Go to, I'll no more on't, it hath made
me mad. I say we will have no moe° marriage. Those that are married already, all but one, shall live. The rest shall keep as they are.

145   To a nunnery, go.

[*Exit.*]

    OPH. O, what a noble mind is here o'erthrown!
        The courtier's, soldier's, scholar's, eye, tongue, sword,
        Th' expectancy° and rose of the fair state,
        The glass° of fashion and the mould of form,
150   Th' observed of all observers, quite quite down!
        And I of ladies most deject and wretched,
        That sucked the honey of his musiced vows,
        Now see that noble and most sovereign reason
        Like sweet bells jangled, out of time and harsh;
155   That unmatched form and feature of blown° youth
        Blasted with ecstasy.° O, woe is me
        T' have seen what I have seen, see what I see!

[*Enter KING and POLONIUS.*]

    KING. Love? His affections° do not that way tend,
        Nor what he spake, though it lacked form a little,
160   Was not like madness. There's something in his soul
        O'er which his melancholy sits on brood,
        And I do doubt° the hatch and the disclose
        Will be some danger; which for to prevent,
        I have in quick determination
165   Thus set it down: he shall with speed to England
        For the demand of our neglected tribute.
        Haply the seas and countries different,
        With variable objects, shall expel

141–142   **make your wantonness your ignorance** excuse your wanton behavior with the plea that you don't know any better

143   **moe** more

148   **expectancy** hope

149   **glass** mirror

155   **blown** blooming

156   **ecstasy** madness

158   **affections** emotions

162   **doubt** fear

This something-settled matter in his heart
170   Whereon his brains still beating puts him thus
From fashion of himself. What think you on't?

POL.   It shall do well. But yet do I believe
The origin and commencement of his grief
Sprung from neglected love.—How now, Ophelia?
175   You need not tell us what Lord Hamlet said,
We heard it all.—My lord, do as you please,
But if you hold it fit, after the play
Let his queen-mother all alone entreat him
To show his grief. Let her be round° with him,
180   And I'll be placed, so please you, in the ear
Of all their conference. If she find him not,
To England send him; or confine him where
Your wisdom best shall think.

KING.   It shall be so.
Madness in great ones must not unwatched go.

[*Exeunt.*]

Scene 2

[*Enter* HAMLET *and three of the* PLAYERS.]

HAM.   Speak the speech, I pray you, as I pronounced it to you,
trippingly on the tongue; but if you mouth it as many of our players
do, I had as lief the town-crier spoke my lines. Nor do not saw the
air too much with your hand thus, but use all gently, for in the
5   very torrent, tempest, and as I may say, whirlwind of your passion,
you must acquire and beget a temperance that may give it smooth-
ness. O, it offends me to the soul to hear a robustious periwig-
pated fellow tear a passion to tatters, to very rags, to split the ears
of the groundlings,° who for the most part are capable of nothing
10   but inexplicable dumb shows and noise. I would have such a fellow whipped for o'erdoing Termagant.° It out-Herods Herod.° Pray
you avoid it.

---

179   **round** plain-spoken
9   **groundlings** spectators who paid least and stood on the ground
11   **Termagant** thought to be a Mohammedan deity, and represented in medieval mystery plays
as a violent and ranting personage
Herod represented in the mystery plays as a blustering tyrant

1 PLAY. I warrant your honour.

HAM. Be not too tame neither, but let your own discretion be your
tutor. Suit the action to the word, the word to the action, with this
special observance, that you o'erstep not the modesty of nature; for
anything so o'erdone is from the purpose of playing, whose end
both at the first, and now, was and is, to hold as 'twere the mirror
up to nature, to show virtue her own feature, scorn her own image,
and the very age and body of the time his form and pressure. Now
this overdone, or come tardy off, though it makes the unskilful
laugh, cannot but make the judicious grieve, the censure° of the
which one must in your allowance o'erweigh a whole theatre of
others. O, there be players that I have seen play—and heard others
praise, and that highly—not to speak it profanely, that neither having th' accent of Christians, nor the gait of Christian, pagan, nor
man, have so strutted and bellowed that I have thought some of
nature's journeymen had made men, and not made them well,
they imitated humanity so abominably.

1 PLAY. I hope we have reformed that indifferently° with us.

HAM. O, reform it altogether. And let those that play your clowns
speak no more than is set down for them, for there be of them that
will themselves laugh, to set on some quantity of barren spectators
to laugh too, though in the meantime some necessary question of
the play be then to be considered. That's villainous, and shows a
most pitiful ambition in the fool that uses it. Go, make you
ready.

[*Exeunt* PLAYERS.]

[*Enter* POLONIUS, GUILDENSTERN, *and* ROSENCRANTZ.]

How now, my lord? Will the king hear this piece of work?

POL. And the queen too, and that presently.

HAM. Bid the players make haste.

[*Exit* POLONIUS.]

Will you two help to hasten them?

ROS. Ay, my lord. [*Exeunt they two.*]

HAM. What, ho, Horatio!

---

22 **censure** judgment, opinion
30 **indifferently** fairly well

[*Enter* HORATIO.]

HOR. Here, sweet lord, at your service.

45 **HAM.** Horatio, thou art e'en as just a man
As e'er my conversation coped° withal.

HOR. O my dear lord!

HAM.   Nay, do not think I flatter,
For what advancement may I hope from thee,
That no revenue hast but thy good spirits
50 To feed and clothe thee? Why should the poor be flattered?
No, let the candied tongue lick absurd pomp,
And crook the pregnant° hinges of the knee
Where thrift° may follow fawning. Dost thou hear?
Since my dear soul was mistress of her choice
55 And could of men distinguish her election,°
S'hath sealed thee for herself, for thou hast been
As one in suff'ring all that suffers nothing,
A man that Fortune's buffets and rewards
Hast ta'en with equal thanks; and blest are those
60 Whose blood and judgment are so well comeddled°
That they are not a pipe for Fortune's finger
To sound what stop she please. Give me that man
That is not passion's slave, and I will wear him
In my heart's core, ay, in my heart of heart,
65 As I do thee. Something too much of this.
There is a play to-night before the king.
One scene of it comes near the circumstance
Which I have told thee of my father's death.
I prithee, when thou seest that act afoot,
70 Even with the very comment of thy soul°
Observe my uncle. If his occulted° guilt
Do not itself unkennel° in one speech,

---

46 **coped** encountered
52 **pregnant** ready
53 **thrift** profit
55 **election** choice
60 **comeddled** mingled
70 **the very comment of thy soul** with a keenness of observation that penetrates to the very
being
71 **occulted** hidden
72 **unkennel** reveal

It is a damnéd ghost that we have seen,
And my imaginations are as foul
75 As Vulcan's stithy.° Give him heedful note,
For I mine eyes will rivet to his face,
And after we will both our judgments join
In censure° of his seeming.

HOR.   Well, my lord.
If 'a steal aught the whilst this play is playing,
80 And 'scape detecting, I will pay the theft.

[*Enter Trumpets and Kettledrums,* KING, QUEEN, POLONIUS, OPHELIA; ROSENCRANTZ, GUILDENSTERN, *and other* LORDS *attendant.*]

HAM. They are coming to the play. I must be idle.°
Get you a place.

KING. How fares our cousin Hamlet?

HAM. Excellent, i' faith, of the chameleon's dish.° I eat the air,
85 promise-crammed. You cannot feed capons so.

KING. I have nothing with this answer, Hamlet. These words are not
mine.

HAM. No, nor mine now. [*To* POLONIUS.] My lord, you played once i'
th' university, you say?

90 **POL.** That did I, my lord, and was accounted a good actor.

HAM. What did you enact?

POL. I did enact Julius Caesar. I was killed i' th' Capitol; Brutus
killed me.

HAM. It was a brute part of him to kill so capital a calf there. Be the
95 players ready?

ROS. Ay, my lord, they stay upon your patience.

QUEEN. Come hither, my dear Hamlet, sit by me.

HAM. No, good mother, here's metal more attractive.

POL. [*To the* KING.] O, ho! do you mark that?

---

75 **stithy** forge
78 **censure** opinion
81 **idle** crazy
84 **chameleon's dish** the air, on which the chameleon was supposed to feed

100   **HAM.** Lady, shall I lie in your lap?

[*Lying down at* OPHELIA'S *feet.*]

       OPH. No, my lord.

       HAM. I mean, my head upon your lap?

       OPH. Ay, my lord.

       HAM. Do you think I meant country matters?

105   **OPH.** I think nothing, my lord.

       HAM. That's a fair thought to lie between maids' legs.

       OPH. What is, my lord?

       HAM. Nothing.

       OPH. You are merry, my lord.

110   **HAM.** Who, I?

       OPH. Ay, my lord.

       HAM. O God, your only jig-maker! What should a man do but be merry? For look you how cheerfully my mother looks, and my father died within's two hours.

115   **OPH.** Nay, 'tis twice two months, my lord.

       HAM. So long? Nay then, let the devil wear black, for I'll have a suit of sables. O heavens! die two months ago, and not forgotten yet? Then there's hope a great man's memory may outlive his life half a year, but by'r lady 'a must build churches then, or else shall
120   'a suffer not thinking on, with the hobby-horse,° whose epitaph is 'For O, for O, the hobby-horse is forgot!'

[*The trumpets sound. Dumb Show follows.*]

---

120   **hobby-horse** the figure of a horse fastened round the waist of a morris dancer. Puritan efforts to suppress the country sports in which the hobby-horse figured led to a popular ballad lamenting the fact that "the hobby-horse is forgot."

[*Enter a* KING *and a* QUEEN, *very lovingly; the* QUEEN *embracing him and he her. She kneels, and makes show of protestation unto him. He takes her up, and declines his head upon her neck. He lies him down upon a bank of flowers; she, seeing him asleep, leaves him. Anon comes in another man, takes off his crown, kisses it, pours poison in the sleeper's ears, and leaves him. The* QUEEN *returns, finds the* KING *dead, makes passionate action. The* POISONER *with some three or four comes in again, seems to condole with her. The dead body is carried away. The* POISONER *woos the* QUEEN *with gifts; she seems harsh awhile, but in the end accepts love. Exeunt.*]

    OPH. What means this, my lord?

    HAM. Marry, this is miching mallecho;° it means mischief.

    OPH. Belike this show imports the argument of the play.

[*Enter* PROLOGUE.]

125   **HAM.** We shall know by this fellow. The players cannot keep counsel; they'll tell all.

    OPH. Will 'a tell us what this show meant?

    HAM. Ay, or any show that you will show him. Be not you ashamed to show, he'll not shame to tell you what it means.

130   **OPH.** You are naught,° you are naught. I'll mark the play.

    PRO.

        For us, and for our tragedy,
        Here stooping to your clemency,
        We beg your hearing patiently.

[*Exit.*]

    HAM. Is this a prologue, or the posy° of a ring?

135   **OPH.** 'Tis brief, my lord.

    HAM. As woman's love.

[*Enter the* PLAYER KING *and* QUEEN.]

    P. KING. *Full thirty times hath Phœbus' cart° gone round*
        Neptune's salt wash and Tellus' orbéd ground,°

---

123   **miching mallecho** skulking or crafty crime
130   **naught** naughty, lewd
134   **posy** brief motto engraved on a finger-ring
137   **Phœbus' cart** the sun's chariot
138   **Tellus' orbed ground** the earth (Tellus was the Roman goddess of the earth)

And thirty dozen moons with borrowed sheen
140   About the world have times twelve thirties been,
Since love our hearts and Hymen° did our hands
Unite comutual in most sacred bands.

    P. QUEEN. *So many journeys may the sun and moon
Make us again count o'er ere love be done!*
145   *But woe is me, you are so sick of late,
So far from cheer and from your former state,
That I distrust° you. Yet though I distrust,
Discomfort you, my lord, it nothing must.
For women's fear and love hold quantity,°*
150   *In neither aught, or in extremity.
Now what my love is proof hath made you know,
And as my love is sized,° my fear is so.
Where love is great, the littlest doubts are fear;
Where little fears grow great, great love grows there.*

155   **P. KING.** *Faith, I must leave thee, love, and shortly too;
My operant° powers their functions leave to do.
And thou shalt live in this fair world behind,
Honored, beloved and haply one as kind
For husband shalt thou—*

    P. QUEEN.   *O, confound the rest!*
160   *Such love must needs be treason in my breast.
In second husband let me be accurst!
None wed the second but who killed the first.*

    HAM. That's wormwood.

    P. QUEEN. *The instances° that second marriage move*
165   *Are base respects of thrift, but none of love.
A second time I kill my husband dead,
When second husband kisses me in bed.*

    P. KING. *I do believe you think what now you speak,
But what we do determine oft we break.*

---

141   **Hymen** god of marriage
147   **distrust** fear for
149   **hold quantity** are proportional, weigh alike
152   **as my love is sized** according to the greatness of my love
156   **operant** vital
164   **instances** motives

170   *Purpose is but the slave to memory,*
   Of violent birth, but poor validity;°
   Which now, the fruit unripe, sticks on the tree,
   But fall unshaken when they mellow be.
   Most necessary 'tis that we forget
175   *To pay ourselves what to ourselves is debt.*
   What to ourselves in passion we propose,
   The passion ending, doth the purpose lose.
   The violence of either grief or joy
   Their own enactures° with themselves destroy.
180   *Where joy most revels, grief doth most lament;*
   Grief joys, joy grieves, on slender accident.
   This world is not for aye,° nor 'tis not strange
   That even our loves should with our fortunes change;
   For 'tis a question left us yet to prove,
185   *Whether love lead fortune, or else fortune love.*
   The great man down, you mark his favorite flies;
   The poor advanced makes friends of enemies;
   And hitherto doth love on fortune tend,
   For who not needs shall never lack a friend,
190   *And who in want a hollow friend doth try,*
   Directly seasons him° his enemy.
   But orderly to end where I begun,
   Our wills and fates do so contrary run
   That our devices still are overthrown;
195   *Our thoughts are ours, their ends none of our own.*
   So think thou wilt no second husband wed,
   But die thy thoughts when thy first lord is dead.

   P. QUEEN. *Nor earth to me give food, nor heaven light,*
   Sport and repose lock from me day and night,
200   *To desperation turn my trust and hope,*
   An anchor's° cheer in prison be my scope,
   Each opposite that blanks the face of joy
   Meet what I would have well, and it destroy,
   Both here and hence pursue me lasting strife,

---

 171 **validity** endurance
 179 **enactures** enactments
 182 **aye** ever
 191 **seasons him** ripens him into
 201 **anchor's** anchorite's

205   *If once a widow, ever I be wife!*

HAM. If she should break it now!

P. KING. *'Tis deeply sworn. Sweet, leave me here awhile.*
My spirits grow dull, and fain I would beguile
The tedious day with sleep.

[*Sleeps.*]

P. QUEEN.   *Sleep rock thy brain,*
210   *And never come mischance between us twain!*

[*Exit.*]

HAM. Madam, how like you this play?

QUEEN. The lady doth protest too much, methinks.

HAM. O, but she'll keep her word.

KING. Have you heard the argument? Is there no offence in't?

215 **HAM.** No, no, they do but jest, poison in jest; no offence i' th' world.

KING. What do you call the play?

HAM. 'The Mouse-trap.' Marry, how? Tropically. This play is the image of a murder done in Vienna. Gonzago is the duke's name; his wife, Baptista. You shall see anon. 'Tis a knavish piece of
220   work, but what of that? Your majesty, and we that have free souls, it touches us not. Let the galled jade° wince, our withers are unwrung.

[*Enter LUCIANUS.*]

This is one Lucianus, nephew to the king.

OPH. You are as good as a chorus, my lord.

225 **HAM.** I could interpret between you and your love, if I could see the puppets dallying.

OPH. You are keen, my lord, you are keen.

HAM. It would cost you a groaning to take off mine edge.

OPH. Still better, and worse.

230 **HAM.** So you mis-take your husbands.—Begin, murderer. Leave thy damnable faces and begin. Come, the croaking raven doth bellow for revenge.

---

221 **galled jade** sorebacked horse

LUC. *Thoughts black, hands apt, drugs fit, and time agreeing,*
       Confederate season, else no creature seeing,
235   *Thou mixture rank, of midnight weeds collected,*
       With Hecate's° ban thrice blasted,° thrice infected,
       Thy natural magic and dire property
       On wholesome life usurps immediately.

[*Pours the poison in his ears.*]

HAM. 'A poisons him i' th' garden for his estate. His name's Gon-
240   zago. The story is extant, and written in very choice Italian. You
       shall see anon how the murderer gets the love of Gonzago's wife.

OPH. The king rises.

HAM. What, frighted with false fire?

QUEEN. How fares my lord?

245 POL. Give o'er the play.

KING. Give me some light. Away!

POL. Lights, lights, lights!

[*Exeunt all but* HAMLET *and* HORATIO.]

HAM.   Why, let the strucken deer go weep,
                 The hart ungallèd play.
250   For some must watch while some must sleep;
                 Thus runs the world away.

       Would not this, sir, and a forest of feathers°—if the rest of my
       fortunes turn Turk with me—with two Provincial roses° on my razed°
       shoes, get me a fellowship in a cry° of players?

255 HOR. Half a share.

HAM. A whole one, I.

                 For thou dost know, O Damon dear,
                 This realm dismantled was

---

236   **Hecate** goddess of witchcraft
       blasted fallen under a blight
252   **feathers** plumes for actors' costumes
253   **Provincial roses** i.e., Provençal roses. Ribbon rosettes resembling these French roses were
       used to decorate shoes.
       razed with ornamental slashing
254   **cry** company

Of Jove himself, and now reigns here
260   A very, very—pajock.°

HOR. You might have rhymed.

HAM. O good Horatio, I'll take the ghost's word for a thousand pound. Didst perceive?

HOR. Very well, my lord.

265 **HAM.** Upon the talk of the poisoning.

HOR. I did very well note him.

HAM. Ah, ha! Come, some music. Come, the recorders.

For if the king like not the comedy,°
Why then, belike he likes it not, perdy.

270   Come, some music.

[*Enter* ROSENCRANTZ *and* GUILDENSTERN.]

GUIL. Good my lord, vouchsafe me a word with you.

HAM. Sir, a whole history.

GUIL. The king, sir—

HAM. Ay, sir, what of him?

275 **GUIL.** Is in his retirement marvellous distempered.

HAM. With drink, sir?

GUIL. No, my lord, with choler.°

HAM. Your wisdom should show itself more richer to signify this to the doctor, for for me to put him to his purgation would perhaps
280   plunge him into more choler.

GUIL. Good my lord, put your discourse into some frame, and start not so wildly from my affair.

HAM. I am tame, sir. Pronounce.

GUIL. The queen your mother, in most great affliction of spirit,
285   hath sent me to you.

HAM. You are welcome.

---

260   **pajock** presumably a variant form of "patchcock," a despicable person. Cf. III.iv. 104

268   **For if . . . comedy** a seeming parody of *The Spanish Tragedy,* IV.i. 197–98 ("And if the world like not this tragedy,/Hard is the hap of old Hieronimo"), where another revenger's dramatic entertainment is referred to

277   **choler** one of the four bodily humors, an excess of which gave rise to anger

GUIL. Nay, good my lord, this courtesy is not of the right breed. If it shall please you to make me a wholesome° answer, I will do your mother's commandment. If not, your pardon and my return shall
290 be the end of my business.

HAM. Sir, I cannot.

ROS. What, my lord?

HAM. Make you a wholesome answer; my wit's diseased. But, sir, such answer as I can make, you shall command, or rather, as you
295 say, my mother. Therefore no more, but to the matter. My mother, you say—

ROS. Then thus she says: your behavior hath struck her into amazement and admiration.

HAM. O wonderful son, that can so stonish a mother! But is there
300 no sequel at the heels of this mother's admiration?° Impart.

ROS. She desires to speak with you in her closet ere you go to bed.

HAM. We shall obey, were she ten times our mother. Have you any further trade with us?

ROS. My lord, you once did love me.

305 HAM. And do still, by these pickers and stealers.°

ROS. Good my lord, what is your cause of distemper? You do surely bar the door upon your own liberty, if you deny your griefs to your friend.

HAM. Sir, I lack advancement.

310 ROS. How can that be, when you have the voice of the king himself for your succession in Denmark?

HAM. Ay, sir, but 'while the grass grows'°—the proverb is something musty.

[Enter the PLAYERS with recorders.]

---

288 **wholesome** reasonable
300 **admiration** wonder
305 **pickers and stealers** hands
312 **"while the grass grows"** a proverb ending "the horse starves"

315 O, the recorders! Let me see one. To withdraw° with you—why do
you go about to recover the wind of me, as if you would drive me
into a toil?°

GUIL. O my lord, if my duty be too bold, my love is too unmannerly.

HAM. I do not well understand that. Will you play upon this
320 pipe?

GUIL. My lord, I cannot.

HAM. I pray you.

GUIL. Believe me, I cannot.

HAM. I do beseech you.

325 GUIL. I know no touch of it, my lord.

HAM. It is as easy as lying. Govern these ventages° with your fingers
and thumb, give it breath with your mouth, and it will discourse
most eloquent music. Look you, these are the stops.

GUIL. But these cannot I command to any utt'rance of harmony. I
330 have not the skill.

HAM. Why, look you now, how unworthy a thing you make of
me! You would play upon me, you would seem to know my stops,
you would pluck out the heart of my mystery, you would sound
me from my lowest note to the top of my compass; and there is
335 much music, excellent voice, in this little organ, yet cannot you
make it speak. 'Sblood, do you think I am easier to be played on than
a pipe? Call me what instrument you will, though you can fret°
me, you cannot play upon me.

[Enter POLONIUS.]

God bless you, sir!

340 POL. My lord, the queen would speak with you, and presently.

HAM. Do you see yonder cloud that's almost in shape of a camel?

POL. By th' mass and 'tis, like a camel indeed.

HAM. Methinks it is like a weasel.

---

314   **withdraw** step aside for private conversation
316   **toil** net, snare
326   **ventages** holes or stops in the recorder
338   **fret** (1) a stop on the fingerboard of a guitar (2) annoy

POL.   It is backed like a weasel.

345   HAM.   Or like a whale.

POL.   Very like a whale.

HAM.   Then I will come to my mother by and by. [*Aside.*] They fool
me to the top of my bent.—I will come by and by.

POL.   I will say so.

[*Exit* POLONIUS.]

350   HAM.   'By and by' is easily said. Leave me, friends.

[*Exeunt all but* HAMLET.]

'Tis now the very witching time of night,
When churchyards yawn, and hell itself breathes out
Contagion to this world. Now could I drink hot blood,
And do such bitter business as the day
355   Would quake to look on. Soft, now to my mother.
O heart, lose not thy nature; let not ever
The soul of Nero° enter this firm bosom.
Let me be cruel, not unnatural;
I will speak daggers to her, but use none.
360   My tongue and soul in this be hypocrites:
How in my words somever° she be shent,°
To give them seals never my soul consent!

[*Exit.*]

Scene 3

[*Enter* KING, ROSENCRANTZ, *and* GUILDENSTERN.]

KING.   I like him not, nor stands it safe with us
To let his madness range. Therefore prepare you.
I your commission will forthwith dispatch,
And he to England shall along with you.
5   The terms of our estate° may not endure
Hazard so near's as doth hourly grow
Out of his brows.°

---

357   **Nero** Roman emperor who murdered his mother
361   **somever** soever
       shent reproved, abused
  5   **terms of our estate** conditions required for our rule as king
  7   **brows** threatening looks that suggest the dangerous plots Hamlet's brain is hatching

GUIL.   We will ourselves provide,
        Most holy and religious fear it is
        To keep those many many bodies safe
10   That live and feed upon your majesty.

ROS.   The single and peculiar° life is bound
        With all the strength and armor of the mind
        To keep itself from noyance,° but much more
        That spirit upon whose weal depends and rests
15   The lives of many. The cess° of majesty
        Dies not alone, but like a gulf doth draw
        What's near it with it. It is a massy wheel
        Fixed on the summit of the highest mount,
        To whose huge spokes ten thousand lesser things
20   Are mortised° and adjoined, which when it falls,
        Each small annexment, petty consequence,
        Attends the boist'rous ruin. Never alone
        Did the king sigh, but with a general groan.

KING.   Arm you, I pray you, to this speedy voyage,
25   For we will fetters put about this fear,
        Which now goes too free-footed.

ROS.   We will haste us.

[*Exeunt Gentlemen.*]

[*Enter POLONIUS.*]

POL.   My lord, he's going to his mother's closet.
        Behind the arras I'll convey myself
        To hear the process. I'll warrant she'll tax him home,
30   And as you said, and wisely was it said,
        'Tis meet that some more audience than a mother,
        Since nature makes them partial, should o'erhear
        The speech of vantage.° Fare you well, my liege.
        I'll call upon you ere you go to bed,
35   And tell you what I know.

KING.   Thanks, dear my lord.

[*Exit POLONIUS.*]

---

11   **peculiar** private
13   **noyance** harm
15   **cess** cessation, extinction
20   **mortised** jointed (as with mortise and tenon)
33   **of vantage** (1) in addition (2) from a convenient place for listening

O, my offence is rank, it smells to heaven;
It hath the primal eldest curse upon't,
A brother's murder. Pray can I not,
Though inclination be as sharp as will.°
40 My stronger guilt defeats my strong intent,
And like a man to double business bound,
I stand in pause where I shall first begin,
And both neglect. What if this cursèd hand
Were thicker than itself with brother's blood,
45 Is there not rain enough in the sweet heavens
To wash it white as snow? Whereto serves mercy
But to confront the visage of offence?
And what's in prayer but this twofold force,
To be forestallèd ere we come to fall,
50 Or pardoned being down? Then I'll look up.
My fault is past. But, O, what form of prayer
Can serve my turn? 'Forgive me my foul murder'?
That cannot be, since I am still possessed
Of those effects for which I did the murder—
55 My crown, mine own ambition, and my queen.
May one be pardoned and retain th' offence?
In the corrupted currents of this world
Offence's gilded hand may shove by justice,
And oft 'tis seen the wicked prize itself
60 Buys out the law. But 'tis not so above.
There is no shuffling;° there the action° lies
In his true nature, and we ourselves compelled,
Even to the teeth and forehead of our faults,
To give in evidence. What then? What rests?
65 Try what repentance can. What can it not?
Yet what can it when one can not repent?
O wretched state! O bosom black as death!
O limèd soul,° that struggling to be free
Art more engaged! Help, angels! Make assay.°
70 Bow, stubborn knees, and heart with strings of steel,

---

39   **will** carnal desire
61   **shuffling** doubledealing
     action legal action
68   **limed soul** caught by sin as the bird by lime
69   **assay** an effort

Be soft as sinews of the new-born babe.
All may be well. [*He kneels.*]

[*Enter* HAMLET.]

HAM. Now might I do it pat, now 'a is a-praying,
And now I'll do't—and so 'a goes to heaven,
75 And so am I revenged. That would be scanned.
A villain kills my father, and for that,
I, his sole son, do this same villain send
To heaven.
Why, this is hire and salary, not revenge.
80 'A took my father grossly,° full of bread,
With all his crimes broad blown, as flush as May;°
And how his audit stands who knows save heaven?
But in our circumstance° and course° of thought
'Tis heavy with him; and am I then revenged
85 To take him in the purging of his soul,
When he is fit and seasoned for his passage?
No.
Up, sword, and know thou a more horrid hent.°
When he is drunk asleep, or in his rage,
90 Or in th' incestuous pleasure of his bed,
At game a-swearing, or about some act
That has no relish of salvation in't—
Then trip him, that his heels may kick at heaven,
And that his soul may be as damned and black
95 As hell, whereto it goes. My mother stays.
This physic but prolongs thy sickly days.

[*Exit.*]

KING. [*Rising.*] My words fly up, my thoughts remain below.
Words without thoughts never to heaven go.

[*Exit.*]

---

80   **grossly** unprepared spiritually
81   **as flush as May** in full flower
83   **in our circumstance** considering all evidence
      course beaten way, habit
88   **hent** occasion, opportunity

Scene 4

[*Enter* QUEEN GERTRUDE *and* POLONIUS.]

POL.　'A will come straight. Look you lay home to him.
Tell him his pranks have been too broad to bear with,
And that your grace hath screen'd and stood between
Much heat and him. I'll silence me even here.
5　Pray you be round.

QUEEN.　　　　　　　　I'll warrant you. Fear me not.
Withdraw, I hear him coming.

[POLONIUS *goes behind the arras.*]

[*Enter* HAMLET.]

HAM.　Now, mother, what's the matter?

QUEEN.　Hamlet, thou hast thy father much offended.

HAM.　Mother, you have my father much offended.

10　QUEEN.　Come, come, you answer with an idle tongue.

HAM.　Go, go, you question with a wicked tongue.

QUEEN.　Why, how now, Hamlet?

HAM.　　　　　　　　　　　What's the matter now?

QUEEN.　Have you forgot me?

HAM.　　　　　　　　　No, by the rood,° not so.
You are the queen, your husband's brother's wife,
15　And would it were not so, you are my mother.

QUEEN.　Nay, then I'll set those to you that can speak.

HAM.　Come, come, and sit you down. You shall not budge.
You go not till I set you up a glass
Where you may see the inmost part of you.

20　QUEEN.　What wilt thou do? Thou wilt not murder me?
Help, ho!

　13　rood cross

POL. [*Behind.*] What, ho! help!

HAM. [*Draws.*] How now, a rat?
    Dead for a ducat, dead!

[*Thrusts his sword through the arras and kills* POLONIUS.]

25   POL. [*Behind.*] O, I am slain!

QUEEN. O me, what hast thou done?

HAM.   Nay, I know not.
    Is it the king?

QUEEN. O, what a rash and bloody deed is this!

HAM. A bloody deed? Almost as bad, good mother,
30   As kill a king and marry with his brother.

QUEEN. As kill a king?

HAM.   Ay, lady, it was my word.
    [*Lifts up the arras and sees the body of* POLONIUS.]
    Thou wretched, rash, intruding fool, farewell!
    I took thee for thy better. Take thy fortune.
    Thou find'st to be too busy is some danger.—
35   Leave wringing of your hands. Peace, sit you down
    And let me wring your heart, for so I shall
    If it be made of penetrable stuff,
    If damnéd custom have not brazed° it so
    That it be proof° and bulwark against sense.

40   QUEEN. What have I done that thou dar'st wag thy tongue
    In noise so rude against me?

HAM.   Such an act
    That blurs the grace and blush of modesty,
    Calls virtue hypocrite, takes off the rose
    From the fair forehead of an innocent love,
45   And sets a blister there, makes marriage-vows
    As false as dicers' oaths. O, such a deed
    As from the body of contraction° plucks
    The very soul, and sweet religion makes
    A rhapsody of words. Heaven's face does glow
50   O'er this solidity and compound mass°

---

38   **brazed** plated it as with brass

39   **proof** impenetrable, as of armor

47   **contraction** the contract of marriage

50   **this solidity and compound mass** the earth, as compounded of the four elements

With heated visage, as against the doom—°
Is thought-sick at the act.

QUEEN.   Ay me, what act,
That roars so loud and thunders in the index?°

HAM.   Look here upon this picture and on this,
55   The counterfeit presentment° of two brothers.
See what a grace was seated on this brow:
Hyperion's curls, the front° of Jove himself,
An eye like Mars, to threaten and command,
A station° like the herald Mercury
60   New lighted on a heaven-kissing hill—
A combination and a form indeed
Where every god did seem to set his seal
To give the world assurance of a man.
This was your husband. Look you now what follows.
65   Here is your husband, like a mildewed ear
Blasting his wholesome brother. Have you eyes?
Could you on this fair mountain leave to feed,
And batten° on this moor? Ha, have you eyes?
You cannot call it love, for at your age
70   The heyday° in the blood is tame, it's humble,
And waits upon the judgment, and what judgment
Would step from this to this? Sense° sure you have,
Else could you not have motion, but sure that sense
Is apoplexed, for madness would not err
75   Nor sense to ecstasy° was ne'er so thralled
But it reserved some quantity of choice
To serve in such a difference. What devil was't
That thus hath cozened you at hoodman-blind?°

---

51   **doom** Judgment Day
53   **index** table of contents; thus, indication of what is to follow
55   **counterfeit presentment** portrait
57   **front** forehead
59   **station** bearing, figure
68   **batten** feed like an animal
70   **heyday** ardor
72   **Sense** the senses collectively, which according to Aristotelian tradition are found in all creatures that have the power of locomotion
75   **ecstasy** madness
78   **hoodman-blind** blindman's bluff

Eyes without feeling, feeling without sight,
80   Ears without hands or eyes, smelling sans° all,
Or but a sickly part of one true sense
Could not so mope.° O shame, where is thy blush?
Rebellious hell,
If thou canst mutine in a matron's bones,
85   To flaming youth let virtue be as wax
And melt in her own fire. Proclaim no shame
When the compulsive ardor gives the charge,
Since frost itself as actively doth burn,
And reason panders will.°

QUEEN.   O Hamlet, speak no more!
90   Thou turn'st my eyes into my very soul,
And there I see such black and grainéd spots°
As will not leave their tinct.°

HAM.   Nay, but to live
In the rank sweat of an enseaméd° bed,
Stewed in corruption, honeying and making love
95   Over the nasty sty—

QUEEN.   O, speak to me no more!
These words like daggers enter in my ears.
No more, sweet Hamlet.

HAM.   A murderer and a villain,
A slave that is not twentieth part of the tithe
Of your precedent lord, a vice° of kings,
100   A cutpurse of the empire and the rule,
That from a shelf the precious diadem stole
And put it in his pocket—

QUEEN. No more.

[Enter GHOST.]

HAM. A king of shreds and patches—

---

80   **sans** without
82   **mope** act without full use of one's wits
89   **will** desire
91   **grained spots** indelible stains
92   **tinct** color
93   **enseaméd** greasy
99   **vice** a character in the morality plays, presented often as a buffoon (here, a caricature)

105   Save me and hover o'er me with your wings,
You heavenly guards! What would your gracious figure?

QUEEN.   Alas, he's mad.

HAM.   Do you not come your tardy son to chide,
That lapsed in time and passion lets go by
110   Th' important acting of your dread command?
O, say!

GHOST.   Do not forget. This visitation
Is but to whet thy almost blunted purpose.
But look, amazement on thy mother sits.
115   O, step between her and her fighting soul!
Conceit° in weakest bodies strongest works.
Speak to her, Hamlet.

HAM.   How is it with you, lady?

QUEEN.   Alas, how is't with you,
That you do bend your eye on vacancy,
120   And with th' incorporal air do hold discourse?
Forth at your eyes your spirits wildly peep,
And as the sleeping soldiers in th' alarm,
Your bedded hair like life in excrements°
Start up and stand an° end. O gentle son,
125   Upon the heat and flame of thy distemper
Sprinkle cool patience. Whereon do you look?

HAM.   On him, on him! Look you how pale he glares.
His form and cause conjoined, preaching to stones,
Would make them capable.°—Do not look upon me,
130   Lest with this piteous action you convert
My stern effects. Then what I have to do
Will want° true color—tears perchance for blood.

QUEEN.   To whom do you speak this?

HAM.   Do you see nothing there?

135 QUEEN.   Nothing at all, yet all that is I see.

HAM.   Nor did you nothing hear?

---

116   **Conceit** imagination
123   **excrements** nails, hair (whatever grows out of the body)
124   **an** on
129   **capable** able to respond
132   **want** lack

QUEEN. No, nothing but ourselves.

HAM. Why, look you there. Look how it steals away.
    My father, in his habit as he lived!
140   Look where he goes even now out at the portal.

[*Exit* GHOST.]

QUEEN. This is the very coinage of your brain.
    This bodiless creation ecstasy
    Is very cunning in.

HAM. My pulse as yours doth temperately keep time,
145   And makes as healthful music. It is not madness
    That I have uttered. Bring me to the test,
    And I the matter will re-word, which madness
    Would gambol° from. Mother, for love of grace,
    Lay not that flattering unction° to your soul,
150   That not your trespass but my madness speaks.
    It will but skin and film the ulcerous place
    Whiles rank corruption, mining° all within,
    Infects unseen. Confess yourself to heaven,
    Repent what's past, avoid what is to come,
155   And do not spread the compost on the weeds,
    To make them ranker. Forgive me this my virtue,
    For in the fatness° of these pursy° times
    Virtue itself of vice must pardon beg,
    Yea, curb and woo for leave to do him good.

160 QUEEN. O Hamlet, thou hast cleft my heart in twain.

HAM. O, throw away the worser part of it,
    And live the purer with the other half.
    Good night—but go not to my uncle's bed.
    Assume a virtue, if you have it not.
165   That monster custom, who all sense doth eat,°

---

148   **gambol** leap or start, as a shying horse
149   **unction** ointment; hence, soothing notion
152   **mining** undermining
157   **fatness** grossness, slackness
        pursy corpulent
165   **who all sense doth eat** who consumes all human sense, both bodily and spiritual

Of habits devil,° is angel yet in this,
That to the use of actions fair and good
He likewise gives a frock or livery
That aptly is put on. Refrain to-night,
170 And that shall lend a kind of easiness
To the next abstinence; the next more easy;
For use almost can change the stamp of nature,
And either curb the devil, or throw him out
With wondrous potency. Once more, good night,
175 And when you are desirous to be blest,
I'll blessing beg of you. For this same lord
I do repent; but heaven hath pleased it so,
To punish me with this, and this with me,
That I must be their scourge and minister.
180 I will bestow him and will answer well
The death I gave him. So, again, good night.
I must be cruel only to be kind.
This° bad begins and worse remains behind.°
One word more, good lady.

QUEEN.   What shall I do?

185 **HAM.** Not this, by no means, that I bid you do:
Let the bloat king tempt you again to bed,
Pinch wanton on your cheek, call you his mouse,
And let him, for a pair of reechy° kisses,
Or paddling in your neck with his damned fingers,
190 Make you to ravel all this matter out,
That I essentially° am not in madness,
But mad in craft. 'Twere good you let him know,
For who that's but a queen, fair, sober, wise,
Would from a paddock,° from a bat, a gib,°

---

166   **Of habits devil** being a devil in, or in respect of, habits (with a play on "habits," as meaning
both settled practices and garments, whereby devilish practices contrast with "actions fair and
good," line 167, and devilish garments contrast with "frock or livery" of line 168, which custom
in its angelic aspect provides)

183   **This** i.e., the death of Polonius (cf. line 178)
remains behind is yet to come

188   **reechy** dirty

191   **essentially** in fact

194   **paddock** toad
gib tom-cat

195 Such dear concernings hide? Who would so do?
No, in despite of sense and secrecy,
Unpeg the basket on the house's top,
Let the birds fly, and like the famous ape,
To try conclusions, in the basket creep
200 And break your own neck down.°

QUEEN. Be thou assured, if words be made of breath
And breath of life, I have no life to breathe
What thou hast said to me.

HAM. I must to England; you know that?

QUEEN. Alack,
205 I had forgot. 'Tis so concluded on.

HAM. There's letters sealed, and my two school-fellows,
Whom I will trust as I will adders fanged,
They bear the mandate; they must sweep my way
And marshal me to knavery. Let it work,
210 For 'tis the sport to have the engineer
Hoist with his own petar;° and't shall go hard
But I will delve one yard below their mines
And blow them at the moon. O, 'tis most sweet
When in one line two crafts directly meet.
215 This man shall set me packing.
I'll lug the guts into the neighbour room.
Mother, good night indeed.° This counsellor
Is now most still, most secret, and most grave,
Who was in life a foolish prating knave.
220 Come sir, to draw toward an end with you.
Good night, mother.

[*Exit* HAMLET *tugging in* POLONIUS.]

197–200 **Unpeg the basket . . . neck down** the story is lost (in it, apparently, the ape carries a cage
of birds to the top of a house, releases them by accident, and, surprised at their flight, imagines
he can imitate it by first creeping into the basket and then leaping out. The moral of the story,
for the queen, is not to expose herself to destruction by making public what good sense
decrees should be kept secret.)

211 **petar** a bomb or charge for blowing in gates

217 **indeed** in earnest (cf. lines 163, 174, 181)

Act 4

Scene 1

[*Enter* KING *to the* QUEEN, *with* ROSENCRANTZ *and* GUILDENSTERN.]

KING.   There's matter in these sighs, these profound heaves,
You must translate;° 'tis fit we understand them.
Where is your son?

QUEEN.   Bestow this place on us a little while.

[*Exeunt* ROSENCRANTZ *and* GUILDENSTERN.]

5   Ah, mine own lord, what have I seen to-night!

KING.   What, Gertrude, how does Hamlet?

QUEEN.   Mad as the sea and wind when both contend
Which is the mightier. In his lawless fit,
Behind the arras hearing something stir,
10   Whips out his rapier, cries 'A rat, a rat!'
And in this brainish apprehension° kills
The unseen good old man.

KING.   O heavy deed!
It had been so with us had we been there.
His liberty is full of threats to all—
15   To you yourself, to us, to every one.
Alas, how shall this bloody deed be answered?
It will be laid to us, whose providence
Should have kept short, restrained, and out of haunt,°

---

2   **translate** explain
11   **brainish apprehension** frenzied delusion
18   **out of haunt** away from society

This mad young man. But so much was our love,
20 We would not understand what was most fit,
But like the owner of a foul disease,
To keep it from divulging, let it feed
Even on the pith of life. Where is he gone?

QUEEN. To draw apart the body he hath killed,
25 O'er whom his very madness, like some ore
Among a mineral° of metals base,
Shows itself pure: 'a weeps for what is done.

KING. O Gertrude, come away!
The sun no sooner shall the mountains touch
30 But we will ship him hence, and this vile deed
We must with all our majesty and skill
Both countenance and excuse. Ho, Guildenstern!

[*Enter ROSENCRANTZ and GUILDENSTERN.*]

Friends both, go join you with some further aid.
Hamlet in madness hath Polonius slain,
35 And from his mother's closet hath he dragged him.
Go seek him out; speak fair, and bring the body
Into the chapel. I pray you haste in this.

[*Exeunt ROSENCRANTZ and GUILDENSTERN.*]

Come, Gertrude, we'll call up our wisest friends
And let them know both what we mean to do
40 And what's untimely done; so haply slander—
Whose whisper o'er the world's diameter,
As level° as the cannon to his blank,°
Transport his poisoned shot—may miss our name,
And hit the woundless air. O, come away!
45 My soul is full of discord and dismay.

[*Exeunt.*]

---

26 **mineral** mine
42 **As level** as sure of aim
blank target

Scene 2

[*Enter* HAMLET.]

  HAM. Safely stowed.—But soft, what noise? Who calls on Hamlet?
   O, here they come.

[*Enter* ROSENCRANTZ, GUILDENSTERN, *and* OTHERS.]

  ROS. What have you done, my lord, with the dead body?

  HAM. Compounded it with dust, whereto 'tis kin.

5 **ROS.** Tell us where 'tis, that we may take it thence
   And bear it to the chapel.

  HAM. Do not believe it.

  ROS. Believe what?

  HAM. That I can keep your counsel and not mine own. Besides,
10 to be demanded of a sponge—what replication° should be made by
   the son of a king?

  ROS. Take you me for a sponge, my lord?

  HAM. Ay, sir, that soaks up the king's countenance, his rewards,
   his authorities. But such officers do the king best service in the
15 end. He keeps them like an apple in the corner of his jaw, first
   mouthed to be last swallowed. When he needs what you have
   gleaned, it is but squeezing you and, sponge, you shall be dry
   again.

  ROS. I understand you not, my lord.

20 **HAM.** I am glad of it. A knavish speech sleeps in a foolish ear.

  ROS. My lord, you must tell us where the body is, and go with us
   to the king.

  HAM. The body is with the king, but the king is not with the body.
   The king is a thing—

25 **GUIL.** A thing, my lord!

  HAM. Of nothing. Bring me to him. Hide fox, and all after.°

[*Exeunt.*]

---

  10 **replication** reply
  26 **Hide fox, and all after** presumably a cry in some game such as hide-and-seek

Scene 3

[*Enter* KING, *and two or three.*]

     KING. I have sent to seek him, and to find the body.
       How dangerous is it that this man goes loose!
       Yet must not we put the strong law on him.
       He's loved of the distracted multitude,
5   Who like not in their judgment but their eyes,
       And where 'tis so, th' offender's scourge is weighed,
       But never the offence. To bear all smooth and even,
       This sudden sending him away must seem
       Deliberate pause.° Diseases desperate grown
10   By desperate appliance are relieved,
       Or not at all.

[*Enter* ROSENCRANTZ, GUILDENSTERN, *and all the rest.*]

               How now! what hath befall'n?

     ROS. Where the dead body is bestowed, my lord,
       We cannot get from him.

     KING.   But where is he?

     ROS. Without, my lord; guarded, to know your pleasure.

15   KING. Bring him before us.

     ROS.   Ho! Bring in the lord.

[*They enter with* HAMLET.]

     KING. Now, Hamlet, where's Polonius?

     HAM. At supper.

     KING. At supper? Where?

     HAM. Not where he eats, but where 'a is eaten. A certain convo-
20   cation of politic worms are e'en at him. Your worm is your only
       emperor for diet. We fat all creatures else to fat us, and we fat
       ourselves for maggots. Your fat king and your lean beggar is but
       variable service—two dishes, but to one table. That's the end.

     KING. Alas, alas!

25   HAM. A man may fish with the worm that hath eat of a king, and eat
       of the fish that hath fed of that worm.

     KING. What dost thou mean by this?

---

9   **Deliberate pause** carefully considered

HAM. Nothing but to show you how a king may go a progress° through the guts of a beggar.

30   **KING.** Where is Polonius?

HAM. In heaven. Send thither to see. If your messenger find him not there, seek him i' th' other place yourself. But if, indeed, you find him not within this month, you shall nose him as you go up the stairs into the lobby.

35   **KING.** [*To* ATTENDANTS.] Go seek him there.

HAM. 'A will stay till you come.

[*Exeunt* ATTENDANTS.]

KING. Hamlet, this deed, for thine especial safety—
Which we do tender,° as we dearly grieve
For that which thou hast done—must send thee hence
40   With fiery quickness. Therefore prepare thyself.
The bark is ready, and the wind at help,
Th' associates tend, and everything is bent
For England.

HAM.   For England?

KING.   Ay, Hamlet.

HAM.   Good.

KING. So is it, if thou knew'st our purposes.

45   **HAM.** I see a cherub° that sees them. But come, for England! Farewell, dear mother.

KING. Thy loving father, Hamlet.

HAM. My mother. Father and mother is man and wife, man and wife is one flesh. So, my mother. Come, for England.

[*Exit.*]

50   **KING.** Follow him at foot; tempt him with speed aboard.
Delay it not; I'll have him hence to-night.
Away! for everything is sealed and done
That else leans on th' affair. Pray you make haste.

[*Exeunt all but the* KING.]

---

28   **progress** the state journey of a ruler

38   **tender** value

45   **cherub** one of the cherubim, the watchmen or sentinels of heaven, and thus endowed with the keenest vision

And, England, if my love thou hold'st at aught—
55 As my great power thereof may give thee sense,
     Since yet thy cicatrice° looks raw and red
     After the Danish sword, and thy free awe
     Pays homage to us—thou mayst not coldly set°
     Our sovereign process,° which imports at full
60 By letters congruing to° that effect
     The present death of Hamlet. Do it, England,
     For like the hectic° in my blood he rages,
     And thou must cure me. Till I know 'tis done,
     Howe'er my haps,° my joys were ne'er begun.

[*Exit.*]

Scene 4

[*Enter* FORTINBRAS *with his* ARMY *over the stage.*]

     FORT. Go, captain, from me greet the Danish king.
     Tell him that by his licence Fortinbras
     Craves the conveyance° of a promised march
     Over his kingdom. You know the rendezvous.
5   If that his majesty would aught with us,
     We shall express our duty in his eye,°
     And let him know so.

     CAP.   I will do't, my lord.

     FORT. Go softly on.

[*Exeunt all but the* CAPTAIN.]

[*Enter* HAMLET, ROSENCRANTZ, GUILDENSTERN, *and* OTHERS.]

     HAM. Good sir, whose powers are these?

10   **CAP.** They are of Norway, sir.

---

56   **cicatrice** scar, used here of memory of a defeat
58   **coldly set** regard with indifference
59   **process** mandate
60   **congruing to** in accordance with
62   **hectic** consumptive fever
64   **haps** fortunes
3   **conveyance** conduct
6   **eye** presence

HAM. How purposed, sir, I pray you?

CAP. Against some part of Poland.

HAM. Who commands them, sir?

CAP. The nephew to old Norway, Fortinbras.

15 **HAM.** Goes it against the main° of Poland, sir,
Or for some frontier?

CAP. Truly to speak, and with no addition,°
We go to gain a little patch of ground
That hath in it no profit but the name.
20 To pay° five ducats, five, I would not farm it;
Nor will it yield to Norway or the Pole
A ranker rate° should it be sold in fee.°

HAM. Why, then the Polack never will defend it.

CAP. Yes, it is already garrisoned.

25 **HAM.** Two thousand souls and twenty thousand ducats
Will not debate the question of this straw.
This is th' imposthume° of much wealth and peace,
That inward breaks, and shows no cause without
Why the man dies. I humbly thank you, sir.

30 **CAP.** God buy you, sir.
[*Exit.*]

ROS.   Will't please you go, my lord?

HAM. I'll be with you straight. Go a little before.
[*Exeunt all but HAMLET.*]

How all occasions do inform° against me,
And spur my dull revenge! What is a man,
If his chief good and market° of his time
35 Be but to sleep and feed? A beast, no more.

---

15   **main** chief part
17   **addition** exaggeration
20   **To pay** i.e., for a yearly rental
22   **a ranker rate** a greater price
     sold in fee sold with absolute and perpetual possession
27   **imposthume** abscess
32   **inform** take shape
34   **market** profit

Sure he that made us with such large discourse,°
Looking before and after, gave us not
That capability and godlike reason
To fust° in us unused. Now, whether it be
40   Bestial oblivion, or some craven scruple
Of thinking too precisely on th' event—
A thought which, quartered, hath but one part wisdom
And ever three parts coward—I do not know
Why yet I live to say 'This thing's to do',
45   Sith I have cause, and will, and strength, and means,
To do't. Examples gross as earth exhort me:
Witness this army of such mass and charge,
Led by a delicate and tender prince,
Whose spirit, with divine ambition puffed,
50   Makes mouths at° the invisible event,
Exposing what is mortal and unsure
To all that fortune, death, and danger dare,
Even for an eggshell. Rightly to be great
Is not to stir without great argument,
55   But greatly to find quarrel in a straw
When honor's at the stake.° How stand I then,
That have a father killed, a mother stained,
Excitements of my reason and my blood,
And let all sleep, while to my shame I see
60   The imminent death of twenty thousand men
That for a fantasy and trick of fame
Go to their graves like beds, fight for a plot
Whereon the numbers cannot try the cause,°
Which is not tomb enough and continent°
65   To hide the slain? O, from this time forth,
My thoughts be bloody, or be nothing worth!

[Exit.]

---

36   **discourse** power of reasoning
39   **fust** grow musty
50   **Makes mouths at** makes scornful faces at, derides
53–56 **Rightly to be great . . . honor's at the stake** i.e., to be rightly great is *not* to refuse to act ("stir") in a dispute ("argument") because the grounds are insufficient, but to be moved to action even in trivial circumstances where a question of honor is involved
63   **try the cause** settle by combat
64   **continent** receptacle

Scene 5

[*Enter* HORATIO, QUEEN GERTRUDE, *and a* GENTLEMAN.]

    QUEEN. I will not speak with her.

    GENT. She is importunate, indeed distract.
       Her mood will needs be pitied.

    QUEEN.   What would she have?

    GENT. She speaks much of her father, says she hears
5   There's tricks i' th' world, and hems, and beats her heart,
       Spurns enviously at straws,° speaks things in doubt
       That carry but half sense. Her speech is nothing,°
       Yet the unshaped use° of it doth move
       The hearers to collection;° they aim° at it,
10   And botch the words up fit to their own thoughts,
       Which, as her winks and nods and gestures yield them,
       Indeed would make one think there might be thought,
       Though nothing sure,° yet much unhappily.

    HOR. 'Twere good she were spoken with, for she may strew
15   Dangerous conjectures in ill-breeding minds.

    QUEEN. Let her come in.

[*Exit* GENTLEMAN.]

    [*Aside.*] To my sick soul, as sin's true nature is,
       Each toy° seems prologue to some great amiss.
       So full of artless jealousy° is guilt,
20   It spills° itself in fearing to be spilt.

[*Enter* OPHELIA, *distracted.*]

    OPH. Where is the beauteous majesty of Denmark?

    QUEEN. How now, Ophelia?

---

6   **Spurns enviously at straws** takes exception, spitefully, to trifles

7   **nothing** nonsense

8   **unshaped use** disordered manner

9   **collection** attempts at shaping meaning
      aim guess

13   **sure** certain

18   **toy** trifle

19   **artless jealousy** ill-concealed suspicion

20   **spills** destroys

OPH.	How should I your true love know [*She sings*.]
	From another one?
25	By his cockle hat° and staff,
	And his sandal shoon.°

QUEEN. Alas, sweet lady, what imports this song?

OPH. Say you? Nay, pray you mark.

	He is dead and gone, lady, [*Song*.]
30	He is dead and gone;
	At his head a grass-green turf,
	At his heels a stone.

    O, ho!

QUEEN. Nay, but Ophelia—

OPH.   Pray you mark.

35   [*Sings*.] White his shroud as the mountain snow—

[*Enter* KING.]

QUEEN. Alas, look here, my lord.

OPH.	Larded° all with sweet flowers; [*Song*]
	Which bewept to the grave did not go
	With true-love showers.

40   KING. How do you, pretty lady?

OPH. Well, good dild you!° They say the owl was a baker's daughter.° Lord, we know what we are, but know not what we may be. God be at your table!

KING. Conceit upon her father.°

45   OPH. Pray let's have no words of this, but when they ask you what it means, say you this:

---

25   **cockle hat** hat bearing a cockle shell, worn by a pilgrim who had been to the shrine of St. James of Compostella, in Spain

26   **shoon** shoes

37   **Larded** garnished, strewn

41   **good dild you** God yield (requite) you

41   **They say the owl was a baker's daughter** allusion to a folktale in which a baker's daughter was transformed into an owl because of her ungenerous behavior (giving short measure) when Christ asked for bread in the baker's shop

44   **Conceit upon her father** i.e., obsessed with her father's death

To-morrow is Saint Valentine's day,   [*Song.*]
    All in the morning betime,°
And I a maid at your window,
    To be your Valentine.
Then up he rose, and donn'd his clo'es,
    And dupped° the chamber-door,
Let in the maid, that out a maid
    Never departed more.

50

55   **KING.** Pretty Ophelia—

OPH. Indeed, without an oath, I'll make an end on't.

[*Sings.*]   By Gis° and by Saint Charity,
    Alack, and fie for shame!
Young men will do't, if they come to't;
    By Cock,° they are to blame.
Quoth she 'Before you tumbled me,
    You promised me to wed'.

60

He answers:

    'So would I 'a done, by yonder sun,
    An thou hadst not come to my bed'.

65

KING. How long hath she been thus?

OPH. I hope all will be well. We must be patient, but I cannot choose but weep to think they would lay him i' th' cold ground. My brother shall know of it, and so I thank you for your good counsel. Come, my coach! Good night, ladies, good night. Sweet ladies, good night, good night.

70

[*Exit.*]

KING. Follow her close; give her good watch, I pray you.

[*Exeunt HORATIO and GENTLEMAN.*]

O, this is the poison of deep grief; it springs
All from her father's death, and now behold!
O Gertrude, Gertrude!
When sorrows come, they come not single spies,

75

---

48   **betime** early
52   **dupped** opened
57   **Gis** Jesus
60   **Cock** corruption of *God*

But in battalions: first, her father slain;
Next, your son gone, and he most violent author
Of his own just remove;° the people muddied,°
80 Thick and unwholesome in their thoughts and whispers
For good Polonius' death; and we have done but greenly°
In hugger-mugger° to inter him; poor Ophelia
Divided from herself and her fair judgment,
Without the which we are pictures, or mere beasts;
85 Last, and as much containing as all these,
Her brother is in secret come from France,
Feeds on his wonder, keeps himself in clouds,°
And wants° not buzzers to infect his ear
With pestilent speeches of his father's death,
90 Wherein necessity, of matter beggared,°
Will nothing stick° our person to arraign
In ear and ear. O my dear Gertrude, this,
Like to a murd'ring piece,° in many places
Gives me superfluous death. Attend,

[A noise within.]

[Enter a MESSENGER.]

95 Where are my Switzers?° Let them guard the door.
What is the matter?

    MESS.   Save yourself, my lord.
The ocean, overpeering of his list,°
Eats not the flats with more impiteous haste

---

79 **remove** banishment, departure
muddied stirred up and confused
81 **greenly** without judgment
82 **hugger-mugger** secrecy and disorder
87 **in clouds** i.e., of suspicion and rumor
88 **wants** lacks
90 **of matter beggared** lacking facts
91 **nothing stick** in no way hesitate
93 **murd'ring piece** cannon loaded with shot meant to scatter
95 **Switzers** Swiss bodyguards
97 **list** boundary

Then young Laertes, in a riotous head,°
100   O'erbears your officers. The rabble call him lord,
        And as the world were now but to begin,
        Antiquity forgot, custom not known,
        The ratifiers and props of every word,
        They cry 'Choose we, Laertes shall be king'.
105   Caps, hands, and tongues, applaud it to the clouds,
        'Laertes shall be king, Laertes king'.

    QUEEN.   How cheerfully on the false trail they cry!

[A noise within.]

        O, this is counter,° you false Danish dogs!

    KING.   The doors are broke.

[Enter LAERTES, with OTHERS.]

110   LAER.   Where is this king?—Sirs, stand you all without.

    ALL.   No, let's come in.

    LAER.   I pray you give me leave.

    ALL.   We will, we will.

[Exeunt his followers.]

    LAER.   I thank you. Keep the door.—O thou vile king,
        Give me my father!

    QUEEN.   Calmly, good Laertes.

115   LAER.   That drop of blood that's calm proclaims me bastard,
        Cried cuckold to my father, brands the harlot
        Even here between the chaste unsmirchéd brow
        Of my true mother.

    KING.   What is the cause, Laertes,
        That thy rebellion looks so giant-like?
120   Let him go, Gertrude. Do not fear° our person.
        There's such divinity doth hedge a king
        That treason can but peep to what it would,
        Acts little of his will. Tell me, Laertes.
        Why thou art thus incensed. Let him go, Gertrude.
125   Speak, man.

---

 99   **riotous head** turbulent mob
108   **counter** hunting backward on the trail
120   **fear** fear for

LAER. Where is my father?

KING.   Dead.

QUEEN. But not by him.

KING.   Let him demand his fill.

LAER. How came he dead? I'll not be juggled with.
    To hell allegiance, vows to the blackest devil,
130   Conscience and grace to the profoundest pit!
    I dare damnation. To this point I stand,
    That both the worlds I give to negligence,
    Let come what comes, only I'll be revenged
    Most throughly° for my father.

135 **KING.** Who shall stay you?

LAER.   My will, not all the world's.
    And for my means, I'll husband them so well
    They shall go far with little.

KING.   Good Laertes,
    If you desire to know the certainty
    Of your dear father, is't writ in your revenge
140   That, swoopstake,° you will draw both friend and foe,
    Winner and loser?

LAER.   None but his enemies.

KING. Will you know them, then?

LAER. To his good friends thus wide I'll ope my arms,
    And like the kind life-rend'ring pelican,°
145   Repast them with my blood.

KING.   Why, now you speak
    Like a good child and a true gentleman.
    That I am guiltless of your father's death,
    And am most sensibly in grief for it,
    It shall as level° to your judgment 'pear
150   As day does to your eye.

[*A noise within.*]

                 'Let her come in.'

---

134 **throughly** thoroughly
140 **swoopstake** sweepstake, taking all the stakes on the gambling table
144 **pelican** supposed to feed her young with her own blood
149 **level** plain

LAER. How now? What noise is that?

[*Enter* OPHELIA.]

O, heat dry up my brains! tears seven times salt
Burn out the sense and virtue° of mine eye!
By heaven, thy madness shall be paid with weight
155 Till our scale turn the beam. O rose of May,
Dear maid, kind sister, sweet Ophelia!
O heavens! is't possible a young maid's wits
Should be as mortal as an old man's life?
Nature is fine° in love, and where 'tis fine
160 It sends some precious instance of itself
After the thing it loves.

> **OPH.** They bore him barefac'd on the bier; [*Song.*]
> Hey non nonny, nonny, hey nonny;
> And in his grave rain'd many a tear—

165 Fare you well, my dove!

LAER. Hadst thou thy wits, and didst persuade revenge,
It could not move thus.

OPH. You must sing 'A-down, a-down,' and you 'Call him a-down-a.'
O, how the wheel° becomes it! It is the false steward, that stole
170 his master's daughter.

LAER. This nothing's more than matter.

OPH. There's rosemary, that's for remembrance. Pray you, love,
remember. And there is pansies, that's for thoughts.

LAER. A document in madness, thoughts and remembrance fitted.

175 **OPH.** There's fennel for you, and columbines. There's rue for you,
and there's some for me. We may call it herb of grace a Sundays.
O, you must wear your rue with a difference. There's a daisy. I
would give you some violets, but they withered all when my father
died. They say 'a made a good end.

180 [*Sings.*] For bonny sweet Robin is all my joy.

---

153 **virtue** power
159 **fine** refined to purity
169 **wheel** burden, refrain

LAER. Thought and affliction, passion, hell itself,
　　　She turns to favor and to prettiness.

OPH.　　　　　And will 'a not come again?　[*Song.*]
　　　　　　　And will 'a not come again?
185　　　　　　　　No, no, he is dead,
　　　　　　　　　Go to thy death-bed,
　　　　　　　　He never will come again.

　　　　　　　His beard was as white as snow,
　　　　　　　All flaxen was his poll;°
190　　　　　　　　He is gone, he is gone,
　　　　　　　　　And we cast away moan:
　　　　　　　God-a-mercy on his soul!

　　　And of all Christian souls, I pray God. God buy you.

[*Exit.*]

LAER.　Do you see this, O God?

195　**KING.**　Laertes, I must commune with your grief,
　　　Or you deny me right. Go but apart,
　　　Make choice of whom your wisest friends you will,
　　　And they shall hear and judge 'twixt you and me.
　　　If by direct or by collateral hand
200　　They find us touched, we will our kingdom give,
　　　Our crown, our life, and all that we call ours,
　　　To you in satisfaction; but if not,
　　　Be you content to lend your patience to us,
　　　And we shall jointly labor with your soul
205　　To give it due content.

LAER.　　　　　　　Let this be so.
　　　His means of death, his obscure funeral—
　　　No trophy, sword, nor hatchment,° o'er his bones,
　　　No noble rite nor formal ostentation—
　　　Cry to be heard, as 'twere from heaven to earth,
210　　That I must call't in question.

189　**poll** head
207　**hatchment** coat of arms

KING.   So you shall;
And where th' offence is, let the great axe fall.
I pray you go with me.

[*Exeunt.*]

Scene 6

[*Enter* HORATIO *and* OTHERS.]

    HOR.   What are they that would speak with me?

    GENTLEMAN.   Sea-faring men, sir. They say they have letters for you.

    HOR.   Let them come in.

[*Exit* GENTLEMAN.]

      I do not know from what part of the world
5   I should be greeted, if not from Lord Hamlet.

[*Enter* SAILORS.]

    SAIL.   God bless you, sir.

    HOR.   Let him bless thee too.

    SAIL.   'A shall, sir, an't please him. There's a letter for you, sir—it
came from th' ambassador that was bound for England—if your
10   name be Horatio, as I am let to know it is.

    HOR.   [*Reads.*] 'Horatio, when thou shalt have overlooked this, give
these fellows some means to the king. They have letters for him.
Ere we were two days old at sea, a pirate of very warlike appoint-
ment gave us chase. Finding ourselves too slow of sail, we put on
15   a compelled valor, and in the grapple I boarded them. On the
instant they got clear of our ship, so I alone became their prisoner.
They have dealt with me like thieves of mercy, but they knew what
they did; I am to do a good turn for them. Let the king have the
letters I have sent, and repair thou to me with as much speed as
20   thou wouldest fly death. I have words to speak in thine ear will
make thee dumb; yet are they much too light for the bore° of
the matter. These good fellows will bring thee where I am.

---

21   **bore** literally, caliber of a gun; hence, size, importance

Rosencrantz and Guildenstern hold their course for England. Of
them I have much to tell thee. Farewell.

25   He that thou knowest thine,
                                                      HAMLET.'

Come, I will give you way for these your letters,
And do't the speedier that you may direct me
To him from whom you brought them.

[*Exeunt.*]

Scene 7

[*Enter* KING *and* LAERTES.]

    KING. Now must your conscience my acquittance seal,
    And you must put me in your heart for friend,
    Sith you have heard, and with a knowing ear,
    That he which hath your noble father slain
5   Pursued my life.

    LAER.   It well appears. But tell me
    Why you proceeded not against these feats,
    So criminal and so capital° in nature,
    As by your safety, greatness, wisdom, all things else,
    You mainly were stirred up.

    KING.   O, for two special reasons,
10   Which may to you, perhaps, seem much unsinewed,°
    But yet to me th' are strong. The queen his mother
    Lives almost by his looks, and for myself—
    My virtue or my plague, be it either which—
    She is so conjunctive° to my life and soul
15   That, as the star moves not but in his sphere,
    I could not but by her. The other motive,
    Why to a public count° I might not go,
    Is the great love the general gender° bear him,

---

   7   **capital** punishable by death
  10 **unsinewed** weak
  14 **conjunctive** closely joined
  17 **count** reckoning
  18 **general gender** common people

Who, dipping all his faults in their affection,
20   Work like the spring that turneth wood to stone,
Convert his gyves° to graces; so that my arrows,
Too slightly timbered for so loud a wind,
Would have reverted to my bow again,
But not where I had aimed them.

25   **LAER.** And so have I a noble father lost,
A sister driven into desp'rate terms,
Whose worth, if praises may go back again,
Stood challenger on mount of all the age
For her perfections. But my revenge will come.

30   **KING.** Break not your sleeps for that. You must not think
That we are made of stuff so flat and dull
That we can let our beard be shook with danger,
And think it pastime. You shortly shall hear more.
I loved your father, and we love our self,
35   And that, I hope, will teach you to imagine—

[*Enter a* MESSENGER *with letters.*]

     MESS. These to your majesty; this to the queen.

     KING. From Hamlet! Who brought them?

     MESS. Sailors, my lord, they say. I saw them not.
They were given me by Claudio; he received them
40   Of him that brought them.

     KING.   Laertes, you shall hear them.—
Leave us.

[*Exit* MESSENGER.]

     [*Reads.*] 'High and mighty, you shall know I am set naked on
your kingdom. To-morrow shall I beg leave to see your kingly eyes,
when I shall, first asking your pardon, thereunto recount the oc-
45   casion of my sudden and more strange return.
                                      HAMLET.'

     What should this mean? Are all the rest come back?
Or is it some abuse, and no such thing?

     LAER. Know you the hand?

---

    21   **gyves** fetters

KING. 'Tis Hamlet's character. 'Naked'!
50   And in a postscript here, he says 'alone'.
        Can you devise° me?

LAER.   I am lost in it, my lord. But let him come.
        It warms the very sickness in my heart
        That I shall live and tell him to his teeth
55   'Thus didest thou.'

KING.   If it be so, Laertes—
        As how should it be so, how otherwise?—
        Will you be ruled by me?

LAER.   Ay, my lord,
        So you will not o'errule me to a peace.

KING.   To thine own peace. If he be now returned,
60   As checking at° his voyage, and that he means
        No more to undertake it, I will work him
        To an exploit now ripe in my device,
        Under the which he shall not choose but fall;
        And for his death no wind of blame shall breathe
65   But even his mother shall uncharge the practice°
        And call it accident.

LAER.   My lord, I will be ruled;
        The rather if you could devise it so
        That I might be the organ.°

KING.   It falls right.
        You have been talked of since your travel much,
70   And that in Hamlet's hearing, for a quality
        Wherein they say you shine. Your sum of parts
        Did not together pluck such envy from him
        As did that one, and that, in my regard,
        Of the unworthiest siege.°

LAER.   What part is that, my lord?

---

51   **devise** explain to
60   **checking at** turning aside from (like a falcon turning from its quarry for other prey)
65   **uncharge the practice** regard the deed as free from villainy
68   **organ** instrument
74   **siege** rank

75   **KING.** A very riband in the cap of youth,
         Yet needful too, for youth no less becomes
         The light and careless livery that it wears
         Than settled age his sables and his weeds,°
         Importing health and graveness. Two months since
80   Here was a gentleman of Normandy.
         I have seen myself, and served against, the French,
         And they can well on horseback, but this gallant
         Had witchcraft in't. He grew unto his seat,
         And to such wondrous doing brought his horse,
85   As had he been incorpsed° and demi-natured°
         With the brave beast. So far he topped° my thought
         That I, in forgery° of shapes and tricks,
         Come short of what he did.

   LAER.   A Norman was't?

   KING. A Norman.

90   **LAER.** Upon my life, Lamord.

   KING.   The very same.

   LAER. I know him well. He is the brooch indeed
         And gem of all the nation.

   KING. He made confession of you,
         And gave you such a masterly report
95   For art and exercise in your defence,
         And for your rapier most especial,
         That he cried out 'twould be a sight indeed
         If one could match you. The scrimers° of their nation
         He swore had neither motion, guard, nor eye,
100   If you opposed them. Sir, this report of his
         Did Hamlet so envenom with his envy
         That he could nothing do but wish and beg
         Your sudden coming o'er, to play with you.
         Now out of this—

   LAER.   What out of this, my lord?

---

78   **weeds** garments
85   **incorpsed** made one body
      demi-natured like a centaur, half man half horse
86   **topped** excelled
87   **forgery** invention
98   **scrimers** fencers (French *escrimeurs*)

105 **KING.** Laertes, was your father dear to you?
Or are you like the painting of a sorrow,
A face without a heart?

LAER.   Why ask you this?

KING. Not that I think you did not love your father,
But that I know love is begun by time,
110 And that I see in passages of proof,°
Time qualifies° the spark and fire of it.
There lives within the very flame of love
A kind of wick or snuff that will abate it,
And nothing is at a like goodness still,
115 For goodness, growing to a plurisy,°
Dies in his own too much. That we would do,
We should do when we would; for this 'would' changes,
And hath abatements and delays as many
As there are tongues, are hands, are accidents,
120 And then this 'should' is like a spendthrift's sigh
That hurts by easing. But to the quick° of th' ulcer—
Hamlet comes back; what would you undertake
To show yourself in deed your father's son
More than in words?

LAER.   To cut his throat i' th' church.

125 **KING.** No place indeed should murder sanctuarize;°
Revenge should have no bounds. But good Laertes,
Will you do this, keep close within your chamber;
Hamlet returned shall know you are come home;
We'll put on those shall praise your excellence,
130 And set a double varnish on the fame
The Frenchman gave you, bring you in fine together,
And wager on your heads. He, being remiss,°
Most generous, and free from all contriving,
Will not peruse° the foils, so that with ease,

---

110 **passages of proof** incidents of experience
111 **qualifies** weakens
115 **plurisy** excess
121 **quick** sensitive flesh
125 **sanctuarize** give sanctuary to
132 **remiss** careless
134 **peruse** inspect

135　Or with a little shuffling, you may choose
　　　A sword unbated,° and in a pass of practice°
　　　Requite him for your father.

　　　　LAER.　　　　　　　　　　I will do't,
　　　And for that purpose I'll anoint my sword.
　　　I bought an unction of a mountebank
140　So mortal that but dip a knife in it,
　　　Where it draws blood no cataplasm° so rare,
　　　Collected from all simples° that have virtue
　　　Under the moon, can save the thing from death
　　　That is but scratched withal. I'll touch my point
145　With this contagion, that if I gall him slightly,
　　　It may be death.

　　　　KING.　　　　　　　Let's further think of this,
　　　Weigh what convenience both of time and means
　　　May fit us to our shape.° If this should fail,
　　　And that our drift° look through our bad performance,
150　'Twere better not assayed. Therefore this project
　　　Should have a back or second° that might hold
　　　If this did blast in proof.° Soft, let me see.
　　　We'll make a solemn wager on your cunnings—
　　　I ha't.
155　When in your motion° you are hot and dry—
　　　As make your bouts more violent to that end—
　　　And that he calls for drink, I'll have preferred° him
　　　A chalice for the nonce,° whereon but sipping,
　　　If he by chance escape your venomed stuck,°
160　Our purpose may hold there.—But stay, what noise?

136	**unbated** not blunted
	pass of practice treacherous thrust
141	**cataplasm** poultice
142	**simples** medicinal herbs
148	**shape** plan
149	**drift** scheme
151	**back or second** something in support
152	**blast in proof** burst during trial (like a faulty cannon)
155	**motion** exertion
157	**preferred** offered to
158	**nonce** occasion
159	**stuck** thrust

[*Enter* QUEEN.]

QUEEN. One woe doth tread upon another's heel,
So fast they follow. Your sister's drowned, Laertes.

LAER. Drowned? O, where?

QUEEN. There is a willow grows askant° the brook
165   That shows his hoar° leaves in the glassy stream.
Therewith fantastic garlands did she make
Of crowflowers, nettles, daisies, and long purples
That liberal° shepherds give a grosser name,
But our cold° maids do dead men's fingers call them.
170   There on the pendent boughs her crownet° weeds
Clamb'ring to hang, an envious° sliver broke,
When down her weedy trophies and herself
Fell in the weeping brook. Her clothes spread wide,
And mermaid-like awhile they bore her up,
175   Which time she chanted snatches of old lauds,°
As one incapable° of her own distress,
Or like a creature native and indued°
Unto that element. But long it could not be
Till that her garments, heavy with their drink,
180   Pulled the poor wretch from her melodious lay
To muddy death.

LAER.   Alas, then she is drowned?

QUEEN. Drowned, drowned.

LAER. Too much of water hast thou, poor Ophelia,
And therefore I forbid my tears; but yet
185   It is our trick; nature her custom holds,
Let shame say what it will. When these are gone,

---

164   **askant** alongside
165   **hoar** gray
168   **liberal** free-spoken, licentious
169   **cold** chaste
170   **crownet** coronet
171   **envious** malicious
175   **lauds** hymns
176   **incapable of** insensible to
177   **indued** endowed

The woman° will be out. Adieu, my lord.
I have a speech o' fire that fain would blaze
But that this folly drowns it.

[*Exit.*]

     KING.   Let's follow, Gertrude.
190   How much I had to do to calm his rage!
Now fear I this will give it start again;
Therefore let's follow.

[*Exeunt.*]

---

187   **woman** unmanly part of nature

Act 5

Scene 1

[*Enter two* CLOWNS.]

CLOWN. Is she to be buried in Christian burial when she wilfully seeks her own salvation?

OTHER. I tell thee she is, therefore make her grave straight. The crowner° hath sat on her, and finds it Christian burial.

5   **CLOWN.** How can that be, unless she drowned herself in her own defence?

OTHER. Why, 'tis found so.

CLOWN. It must be 'se offendendo',° it cannot be else. For here lies the point: if I drown myself wittingly, it argues an act, and an act
10   hath three branches—it is to act, to do, to perform; argal,° she drowned herself wittingly.

OTHER. Nay, but hear you, Goodman Delver.

CLOWN. Give me leave. Here lies the water; good. Here stands the man; good. If the man go to this water and drown himself, it is,
15   will he, nill he, he goes—mark you that. But if the water come to him and drown him, he drowns not himself. Argal, he that is not guilty of his own death shortens not his own life.

OTHER. But is this law?

CLOWN. Ay, marry, is't; crowner's quest° law.

20   **OTHER.** Will you ha' the truth on't? If this had not been a gentle-woman, she should have been buried out o' Christian burial.

0.1   **clowns** rustics
4   **crowner** coroner
8   **se offendendo** the Clown's blunder for *se defendendo* ("in self-defense")
10   **argal** therefore (corrupt form of *ergo*)
19   **quest** inquest

CLOWN. Why, there thou say'st. And the more pity that great folk
should have count'nance in this world to drown or hang themselves more than their even-Christen.° Come, my spade. There is
25   no ancient gentlemen but gard'ners, ditchers, and grave-makers.
They hold up Adam's profession.

OTHER. Was he a gentleman?

CLOWN. 'A was the first that ever bore arms.

OTHER. Why, he had none.

30   CLOWN. What, art a heathen? How dost thou understand the Scripture? The Scripture says Adam digged. Could he dig without arms?
I'll put another question to thee. If thou answerest me not to the
purpose, confess thyself—

OTHER. Go to.

35   CLOWN. What is he that builds stronger than either the mason, the
shipwright, or the carpenter?

OTHER. The gallows-maker, for that frame outlives a thousand tenants.

CLOWN. I like thy wit well, in good faith. The gallows does well. But
40   how does it well? It does well to those that do ill. Now thou dost
ill to say the gallows is built stronger than the church. Argal, the
gallows may do well to thee. To't again, come.

OTHER. Who builds stronger than a mason, a shipwright, or a carpenter?

45   CLOWN. Ay tell me that, and unyoke.°

OTHER. Marry, now I can tell.

CLOWN. To't.

OTHER. Mass, I cannot tell.

[Enter HAMLET and HORATIO afar off.]

CLOWN. Cudgel thy brains no more about it, for your dull ass will
50   not mend his pace with beating. And when you are asked this
question next, say 'a grave-maker.' The houses he makes lasts till
doomsday. Go, get thee in, and fetch me a stoup° of liquor.

[Exit OTHER CLOWN.]

---

24   **even-Christen** fellow Christian
45   **tell me that, and unyoke** answer the question and then you can relax
52   **stoup** tankard

[*HAMLET and* HORATIO *come forward as* CLOWN *digs and sings.*]

> In youth, when I did love, did love, [*Song.*]
> Methought it was very sweet,
55   To contract-O-the time for-a-my behove,°
> O, methought there-a-was nothing-a-meet.°

HAM. Has this fellow no feeling of his business, that 'a sings in
grave-making?

HOR. Custom hath made it in him a property of easiness.°

60 **HAM.** 'Tis e'en so. The hand of little employment hath the daintier
sense.

CLOWN.   But age, with his stealing steps, [*Song.*]
> Hath clawed me in his clutch,
> And hath shipped me into the land,
65   As if I had never been such.

[*Throws up a skull.*]

HAM. That skull had a tongue in it, and could sing once. How the
knave jowls° it to the ground, as if 'twere Cain's jawbone, that
did the first murder! This might be the pate of a politician, which
this ass now o'erreaches; one that would circumvent° God, might it
70 not?

HOR. It might, my lord.

HAM. Or of a courtier, which could say, 'Good morrow, sweet lord!
How does thou, sweet lord?' This might be my Lord Such-a-one,
that praised my Lord Such-a-one's horse, when 'a went to beg it,
75 might it not?

HOR. Ay, my lord.

HAM. Why, e'en so, and now my Lady Worm's, chopless,° and
knock'd abut the mazzard° with a sexton's spade. Here's fine

---

55   **behove** benefit

55-56 The repeated *a* and *o* may represent the Clown's vocal embellishments, but more probably
they represent his grunting as he takes breath in the course of his digging.

59   **a property of easiness** a habit that comes easily to him

67   **jowls** hurls

69   **circumvent** cheat

77   **chopless** with lower jaw missing

78   **mazzard** head

revolution, an we had the trick to see't. Did these bones cost no more
80 the breeding but to play at loggats° with them? Mine ache to think
on't.

CLOWN.   A pick-axe and a spade, a spade, [*Song.*]
                      For and a shrouding sheet;
                  O, a pit of clay for to be made
85   For such a guest is meet.

[*Throws up another skull.*]

HAM.   There's another. Why may not that be the skull of a lawyer?
Where be his quiddities° now, his quillets,° his cases, his tenures,
and his tricks? Why does he suffer this mad knave now to knock
him about the sconce with a dirty shovel, and will not tell him of
90 his action of battery? Hum! This fellow might be in's time a great
buyer of land, with his statutes, his recognizances,° his fines, his
double vouchers,° his recoveries.° Is this the fine of his fines, and
the recovery of his recoveries, to have his fine pate full of fine dirt?
Will his vouchers vouch him no more of his purchases, and dou-
95 ble ones too, than the length and breadth of a pair of indentures?°
The very conveyances° of his lands will scarcely lie in this box, and
must th' inheritor himself have no more, ha?

HOR.   Not a jot more, my lord.

HAM.   Is not parchment made of sheepskins?

100 HOR.   Ay, my lord, and of calves' skins too.

HAM.   They are sheep and calves which seek out assurance in that.
  ✗   I will speak to this fellow. Whose grave's this, sirrah?

CLOWN.   Mine, sir.
              [*Sings.*] O, a pit of clay for to be made—

105 · HAM.   I think it be thine indeed, for thou liest in't.

---

80 **loggats** small logs of wood for throwing at a mark
87 **quiddities** subtle distinctions
    quillets quibbles
91 **recognizances** legal bonds, defining debts
92 **vouchers** persons vouched or called on to warrant a title
    recoveries legal processes to break an entail
95 **pair of indentures** deed or legal agreement in duplicate
96 **conveyances** deeds by which property is transferred

CLOWN. You lie out on't, sir, and therefore 'tis not yours. For my part, I do not lie in't, yet it is mine.

HAM. Thou dost lie in't, to be in't and say it is thine. 'Tis for the dead, not for the quick; therefore thou liest.

110 **CLOWN.** 'Tis a quick lie, sir; 'twill away again from me to you.

HAM. What man dost thou dig it for?

CLOWN. For no man, sir.

HAM. What woman, then?

CLOWN. For none neither.

115 **HAM.** Who is to be buried in't?

CLOWN. One that was a woman, sir; but, rest her soul, she's dead.

HAM. How absolute° the knave is! We must speak by the card,° or equivocation will undo us. By the Lord, Horatio, this three years I have took note of it, the age is grown so picked° that the toe of the
120 peasant comes so near the heel of the courtier, he galls his kibe.° How long hast thou been grave-maker?

CLOWN. Of all the days i' th' year, I came to't that day that our last King Hamlet overcame Fortinbras.

HAM. How long is that since?

125 **CLOWN.** Cannot you tell that? Every fool can tell that. It was that very day that young Hamlet was born—he that is mad, and sent into England.

HAM. Ay, marry, why was he sent into England?

CLOWN. Why, because 'a was mad. 'A shall recover his wits there;
130 or, if 'a do not, 'tis no great matter there.

HAM. Why?

CLOWN. 'Twill not be seen in him there. There the men are as mad as he.

HAM. How came he mad?

135 **CLOWN.** Very strangely, they say.

---

117 **absolute** positive
card card on which the points of the mariner's compass are marked (i.e., absolutely to the point)
119 **picked** fastidious
120 **kibe** chilblain

HAM. How strangely?

CLOWN. Faith, e'en with losing his wits.

HAM. Upon what ground?

CLOWN. Why, here in Denmark. I have been sexton here, man and
140   boy, thirty years.

HAM. How long will a man lie i' th' earth ere he rot?

CLOWN. Faith, if 'a be not rotten before 'a die—as we have many
pocky° corses now-a-days that will scarce hold the laying in—'a will
last you some eight year or nine year. A tanner will last you nine
145   year.

HAM. Why he more than another?

CLOWN. Why, sir, his hide is so tanned with his trade that 'a will
keep out water a great while; and your water is a sore decayer of
your whoreson dead body. Here's a skull now hath lien you i' th'
150   earth three and twenty years.

HAM. Whose was it?

CLOWN. A whoreson mad fellow's it was. Whose do you think it
was?

HAM. Nay, I know not.

CLOWN. A pestilence on him for a mad rogue! 'A poured a flagon of
155   Rhenish° on my head once. This same skull, sir, was, sir, Yorick's
skull, the king's jester.

HAM. [*Takes the skull.*] This?

CLOWN. E'en that.

HAM. Alas, poor Yorick! I knew him, Horatio—a fellow of infinite
160   jest, of most excellent fancy. He hath bore me on his back a thousand times, and now how abhorred in my imagination it is! My
gorge rises at it. Here hung those lips that I have kissed I know not
how oft. Where be your gibes now, your gambols, your songs,
your flashes of merriment that were wont to set the table on a roar?
165   Not one now to mock your own grinning? Quite chop-fall'n? Now
get you to my lady's chamber, and tell her, let her paint an inch

---

143   **pocky** infected with pox (syphillis)
155   **Rhenish** Rhine wine

thick, to this favor she must come. Make her laugh at that.
Prithee, Horatio, tell me one thing.

HOR. What's that, my lord?

170 **HAM.** Dost thou think Alexander looked o' this fashion i' th' earth?

HOR. E'en so.

HAM. And smelt so? Pah! [*Throws down the skull.*]

HOR. E'en so, my lord.

HAM. To what base uses we may return, Horatio! Why may not
175 imagination trace the noble dust of Alexander till 'a find it stopping
a bung-hole?

HOR. 'Twere to consider too curiously° to consider so.

HAM. No, faith, not a jot, but to follow him thither with modesty
enough, and likelihood to lead it. Alexander died, Alexander was
180 buried, Alexander returneth to dust; the dust is earth; of earth we
make loam; and why of that loam whereto he was converted might
they not stop a beer-barrel?

Imperious Cæsar, dead and turned to clay,
Might stop a hole to keep the wind away.
185 O, that that earth which kept the world in awe
Should patch a wall t'expel the winter's flaw!°

But soft, but soft awhile! Here comes the king,
The queen, the courtiers.

[*Enter* KING, QUEEN, LAERTES, *and the Corse with a Doctor of Divinity as* PRIEST
and LORDS *attendant.*]

Who is this they follow?
And with such maiméd rites? This doth betoken
190 The corse they follow did with desperate hand
Fordo° it° own life. 'Twas of some estate.
Couch we awhile and mark.

[*Retires with* HORATIO.]

LAER. What ceremony else?

HAM. That is Laertes, a very noble youth. Mark.

---

177 **too curiously** over ingeniously
186 **flaw** gust
191 **Fordo** destroy
     it its

195   **LAER.** What ceremony else?

  DOCTOR. Her obsequies have been as far enlarged
    As we have warranty. Her death was doubtful,
    And but that great command o'ersways the order,
    She should in ground unsanctified been lodged
200   Till the last trumpet. For charitable prayers,
    Shards,° flints, and pebbles, should be thrown on her.
    Yet here she is allowed her virgin crants,°
    Her maiden strewments, and the bringing home
    Of bell and burial.

205   **LAER.** Must there no more be done?

  DOCTOR.   No more be done.
    We should profane the service of the dead
    To sing a requiem and such rest to her
    As to peace-parted souls.

  LAER.   Lay her i' th' earth,
    And from her fair and unpolluted flesh
210   May violets spring! I tell thee, churlish priest,
    A minist'ring angel shall my sister be
    When thou liest howling.

  HAM.   What, the fair Ophelia!

  QUEEN. Sweets to the sweet. Farewell! [*Scatters flowers.*]
    I hoped thou shouldst have been my Hamlet's wife.
215   I thought thy bride-bed to have decked, sweet maid,
    And not have strewed thy grave.

  LAER.   O, treble woe
    Fall ten times treble on that cursèd head
    Whose wicked deed thy most ingenious° sense
    Deprived thee of! Hold off the earth awhile,
220   Till I have caught her once more in mine arms.

[*Leaps into the grave.*]

    Now pile your dust upon the quick and dead,
    Till of this flat a mountain you have made

---

201   **Shards** bits of broken pottery
202   **crants** garland
218   **most ingenious** of quickest apprehension

T' o'er-top old Pelion° or the skyish head
Of blue Olympus.

HAM. [*Coming forward.*] What is he whose grief
225 Bears such an emphasis,° whose phrase of sorrow
Conjures the wand'ring stars, and makes them stand
Lie wonder-wounded hearers? This is I,
Hamlet the Dane.

[*LAERTES climbs out of the grave.*]

LAER. The devil take thy soul! [*Grappling with him.*]

HAM.   Thou pray'st not well.
230 I prithee take thy fingers from my throat,
For though I am not splenitive° and rash,
Yet have I in me something dangerous,
Which let thy wisdom fear. Hold off thy hand.

KING. Pluck them asunder.

235 **QUEEN.** Hamlet! Hamlet!

ALL. Gentlemen!

HOR. Good my lord, be quiet.

[*The ATTENDANTS part them.*]

HAM. Why, I will fight with him upon this theme
Until my eyelids will no longer wag.

240 **QUEEN.** O my son, what theme?

HAM. I loved Ophelia. Forty thousand brothers
Could not with all their quantity of love
Make up my sum. What wilt thou do for her?

KING. O, he is mad, Laertes.

245 **QUEEN.** For love of God, forbear him.

HAM. 'Swounds, show me what thou't do.
Woo't° weep, woo't fight, woo't fast, woo't tear thyself,
Woo't drink up eisel,° eat a crocodile?

---

223 **Pelion** a mountain in Thessaly, like Olympus, line 224, and Ossa, line 255 (the allusion is to the war in which the Titans fought the gods and, in their attempt to scale heaven, heaped Ossa and Olympus on Pelion, or Pelion and Ossa on Olympus)
225 **such an emphasis** so vehement an expression or display
231 **splenitive** fiery-tempered (from the spleen, seat of anger)
247 **Woo't** wilt (thou)
248 **eisel** vinegar

I'll do't. Dost come here to whine?
250 To outface me with leaping in her grave?
Be buried quick with her, and so will I.
And if thou prate of mountains, let them throw
Millions of acres on us, till our ground,
Singeing his pate against the burning zone,
255 Make Ossa like a wart! Nay, an thou'lt mouth,
I'll rant as well as thou.

QUEEN.   This is mere madness;
And thus awhile the fit will work on him.
Anon, as patient as the female dove
When that her golden couplets° are disclosed,
260 His silence will sit drooping.

HAM.   Hear you, sir.
What is the reason that you use me thus?
I loved you ever. But it is no matter.
Let Hercules himself do what he may,
The cat will mew, and dog will have his day.

265 KING. I pray thee, good Horatio, wait upon him.

[Exit HAMLET and HORATIO.]

[To LAERTES.] Strengthen your patience in our last night's speech.
We'll put the matter to the present push.—
Good Gertrude, set some watch over your son.—
This grave shall have a living monument.
270 An hour of quiet shortly shall we see;
Till then in patience our proceeding be.

[Exeunt.]

Scene 2

[Enter HAMLET and HORATIO.]

HAM. So much for this, sir; now shall you see the other.
You do remember all the circumstance?

HOR. Remember it, my lord!

HAM. Sir, in my heart there was a kind of fighting
5 That would not let me sleep. Methought I lay

---

259   couplets newly-hatched pair

Worse than the mutines° in the bilboes.° Rashly,
And praised be rashness for it—let us know,
Our indiscretion sometime serves us well,
When our deep plots do pall;° and that should learn us
10   There's a divinity that shapes our ends,
Rough-hew them how we will—

HOR.   That is most certain.

HAM. Up from my cabin,
My sea-gown scarfed about me, in the dark
Groped I to find out them, had my desire,
15   Fingered° their packet, and in fine withdrew
To mine own room again, making so bold,
My fears forgetting manners, to unseal
Their grand commission; where I found, Horatio—
Ah, royal knavery!—an exact command,
20   Larded° with many several sorts of reasons,
Importing Denmark's health, and England's too,
With, ho! such bugs and goblins° in my life,
That on the supervise,° no leisure bated,°
No, not to stay° the grinding of the axe,
25   My head should be struck off.

HOR.   Is't possible?

HAM. Here's the commission; read it at more leisure.
But wilt thou hear now how I did proceed?

HOR. I beseech you.

HAM. Being thus benetted round with villainies,
30   Or° I could make a prologue to my brains,
They had begun the play. I sat me down,
Devised a new commission, wrote it fair.

6	**mutines** mutineers
	bilboes fetters
9	**pall** fail
15	**Fingered** filched
20	**Larded** garnished
22	**bugs and goblins** imaginary horrors (here, horrendous crimes attributed to Hamlet, and represented as dangers should he be allowed to live)
23	**supervise** perusal
	bated deducted, allowed
24	**stay** await
30	**Or** ere

I once did hold it, as our statists° do,
A baseness to write fair, and labored much
35 How to forget that learning; but sir, now
It did me yeoman's service. Wilt thou know
Th' effect of what I wrote?

HOR.   Ay, good my lord.

HAM.   An earnest conjuration from the king,
As England was his faithful tributary,
40 As love between them like the palm might flourish,
As peace should still her wheaten garland wear
And stand a comma° 'tween their amities,
And many such like as's of great charge,°
That on the view and knowing of these contents,
45 Without debatement further more or less,
He should those bearers put to sudden death,
Not shriving-time allowed.

HOR.   How was this sealed?

HAM.   Why, even in that was heaven ordinant,°
I had my father's signet in my purse,
50 Which was the model of that Danish seal,
Folded the writ up in the form of th' other,
Subscribed° it, gave't th' impression, placed it safely,
The changeling never known. Now, the next day
Was our sea-fight, and what to this was sequent
55 Thou knowest already.

HOR.   So Guildenstern and Rosencrantz go to't.

HAM.   Why, man, they did make love to this employment.
They are not near my conscience; their defeat
Does by their own insinuation° grow.
60 'Tis dangerous when the baser nature comes

---

33   **statists** statesmen
42   **comma** a connective that also acknowledges separateness
43   **charge** (1) importance (2) burden (the double meaning fits the play that makes "as's" into "asses")
48   **ordinant** guiding
52   **Subscribed** signed
59   **insinuation** intrusion

Between the pass° and fell incensèd points
Of mighty opposites.

HOR.   Why, what a king is this!

HAM. Does it not, think thee, stand me now upon—°
He that hath killed my king and whored my mother,
65   Popped in between th' election° and my hopes,
Thrown out his angle° for my proper° life,
And with such coz'nage—is't not perfect conscience
To quit° him with this arm? And is't not be damned
To let this canker of our nature come
70   In further evil?

HOR. It must be shortly known to him from England
What is the issue of the business there.

HAM. It will be short; the interim is mine.
And a man's life's no more than to say 'one'.
75   But I am very sorry, good Horatio,
That to Laertes I forgot myself;
For by the image of my cause I see
The portraiture of his. I'll court his favours.
But sure the bravery° of his grief did put me
80   Into a tow'ring passion.

HOR.   Peace; who comes here?

[*Enter* OSRIC, *a courtier.*]

OSR. Your lordship is right welcome back to Denmark.

HAM. I humbly thank you, sir. [*Aside to* HORATIO.] Dost know this
water-fly?

HOR. [*Aside to* HAMLET.] No, my good lord.

85   **HAM.** [*Aside to* HORATIO.] Thy state is the more gracious, for 'tis a
vice to know him. He hath much land, and fertile. Let a beast be

---

61   **pass** thrust
      fell fierce
63   **Does it not . . . stand me now upon** is it not incumbent upon me
65   **election** i.e., to the kingship, Denmark being an elective monarchy
66   **angle** fishing line
      proper own
68   **quit** repay
79   **bravery** ostentatious display

lord of beasts, and his crib shall stand at the king's mess.° 'Tis a chough,° but as I say, spacious in the possession of dirt.

OSR. Sweet lord, if your lordship were at leisure, I should impart a thing to you from his majesty.

HAM. I will receive it, sir, with all diligence of spirit. Put your bonnet to his right use. 'Tis for the head.

OSR. I thank your lordship, it is very hot.

HAM. No, believe me, 'tis very cold; the wind is northerly.

OSR. It is indifferent° cold, my lord, indeed.

HAM. But yet methinks it is very sultry and hot for my complexion.°

OSR. Exceedingly, my lord; it is very sultry, as 'twere—I cannot tell how. My lord, his majesty bade me signify to you that 'a has laid a great wager on your head. Sir, this is the matter—

HAM. I beseech you, remember.

[HAMLET moves him to put on his hat.]

OSR. Nay, good my lord; for my ease, in good faith. Sir, here is newly come to court Laertes; believe me, an absolute gentleman, full of most excellent differences,° of very soft society and great showing.° Indeed, to speak feelingly of him, he is the card° or calendar of gentry, for you shall find in him the continent° of what part a gentleman would see.

HAM. Sir, his definement° suffers no perdition in you, though I know to divide him inventorially° would dozy° th' arithmetic of memory, and yet but yaw° neither in respect of his quick sail. But in the

---

87 **mess** table
88 **chough** jackdaw; thus, a chatterer
95 **indifferent** somewhat
96 **complexion** temperament
103 **differences** distinguishing qualities
103–104 **great showing** distinguished appearance
104 **card** map
105 **continent** all-containing embodiment
107 **definement** definition
108 **divide him inventorially** classify him in detail
    dozy dizzy
109 **yaw** hold to a course unsteadily like a ship that steers wild

110   verity of extolment, I take him to be a soul of great article,° and
his infusion° of such dearth° and rareness as, to make true diction
of him, his semblable° is his mirror, and who else would trace° him,
his umbrage,° nothing more.

OSR.   Your lordship speaks most infallibly of him.

115 **HAM.**   The concernancy,° sir? Why do we wrap the gentleman in our
more rawer breath?

OSR.   Sir?

HOR.   Is't not possible to understand in another tongue? You will
to't,° sir, really.

120 **HAM.**   What imports the nomination° of this gentleman?

OSR.   Of Laertes?

HOR.   [*Aside.*] His purse is empty already. All's golden words are
spent.

HAM.   Of him, sir.

125 **OSR.**   I know you are not ignorant—

HAM.   I would you did, sir; yet, in faith, if you did, it would not
much approve° me. Well, sir.

OSR.   You are not ignorant of what excellence Laertes is—

HAM.   I dare not confess that, lest I should compare° with him in
130   excellence; but to know a man well were to know himself.

OSR.   I mean, sir, for his weapon; but in the imputation laid on him
by them in his meed,° he's unfellowed.°

HAM.   What's his weapon?

---

110   **article** scope, importance
111   **infusion** essence
      dearth scarcity
112   **semblable** likeness
      trace (1) draw (2) follow
113   **umbrage** shadow
115   **concernancy** import, relevance
119   **to't** i.e., get to an understanding
120   **nomination** mention
127   **approve** commend
129   **compare** compete
132   **meed** pay
      unfellowed unequaled

OSR. Rapier and dagger.

135   **HAM.** That's two of his weapons—but well.

OSR. The king, sir, hath wagered with him six Barbary horses, against the which he has impawned,° as I take it, six French rapiers and poniards, with their assigns,° as girdle, hangers, and so. Three of the carriages, in faith, are very dear to fancy, very responsive to the

140   hilts, most delicate carriages,° and of very liberal conceit.°

HAM. What call you the carriages?

HOR. [*Aside to* HAMLET.] I knew you must be edified by the margent° ere you had done.

OSR. The carriages, sir, are the hangers.

145   **HAM.** The phrase would be more germane to the matter if we could carry a cannon by our sides. I would it might be hangers till then. But on! Six Barbary horses against six French swords, their assigns, and three liberal conceited carriages; that's the French bet against the Danish. Why is this all impawned, as you call it?

150   **OSR.** The king, sir, hath laid, sir, that in a dozen passes between yourself and him he shall not exceed you three hits;° he hath laid on twelve for nine,° and it would come to immediate trial if your lordship would vouchsafe the answer.

HAM. How if I answer no?

155   **OSR.** I mean, my lord, the opposition of your person in trial.

HAM. Sir, I will walk here in the hall. If it please his majesty, it is the breathing time° of day with me. Let the foils be brought, the gentleman willing, and the king hold his purpose; I will win for him an° I can. If not, I will gain nothing but my shame and the

---

137   **impawned** staked

138   **assigns** appendages

140   **carriages** an affected word for *hangers*, i.e., straps from which the weapon was hung
       liberal conceit elaborate design

142   **margent** margin (where explanatory notes were printed)

150–151   **in a dozen passes . . . he shall not exceed you three hits** the odds the King proposes seem to be that in a match of twelve bouts, Hamlet will win at least five. Laertes would need to win by at least eight to four.

151–152   **he hath laid on twelve for nine** "he" apparently is Laertes, who has seemingly raised the odds against himself by wagering that out of twelve bouts he will win nine

157   **breathing time** time for taking exercise

159   **an** if

160   odd hits.

OSR. Shall I deliver you so?

HAM. To this effect, sir, after what flourish your nature will.

OSR. I commend my duty to your lordship.

HAM. Yours. [*Exit* OSRIC.] He does well to commend it himself;
165   there are no tongues else for's turn.

HOR. This lapwing° runs away with the shell on his head.

HAM. 'A did comply,° sir, with his dug° before 'a sucked it. Thus has
he, and many more of the same bevy° that I know the drossy° age
dotes on, only got the tune of the time; and out of an habit of
170   encounter,° a kind of yesty collection° which carries them through
and through the most fanned and winnowed° opinions; and do but
blow them to their trial, the bubbles are out.

[*Enter a* LORD.]

LORD. My lord, his majesty commended him to you by young Osric,
who brings back to him that you attend him in the hall. He sends
175   to know if your pleasure hold to play with Laertes, or that you will
take longer time.

HAM. I am constant to my purposes; they follow the king's pleasure.
If his fitness° speaks, mine is ready; now or whensoever, provided I
be so able as now.

180 **LORD.** The king and queen and all are coming down.

HAM. In happy time.

LORD. The queen desires you to use some gentle entertainment to
Laertes before you fall to play.

HAM. She well instructs me.

[*Exit* LORD.]

---

166   **lapwing** a bird reputedly so precocious as to run as soon as hatched
167   **comply** observe the formalities of courtesy
        dug mother's nipple
168   **bevy** a covey of quails or lapwings
        drossy frivolous
170   **encounter** manner of address or accosting
        yesty collection a frothy and superficial patchwork of terms from the conversation of others
171   **winnowed** tested, freed from inferior elements
178   **fitness** convenience, inclination

185   **HOR.** You will lose, my lord.

      HAM. I do not think so. Since he went into France I have been in continual practice. I shall win at the odds. But thou wouldst not think how ill all's here about my heart. But it is no matter.

      HOR. Nay, good my lord—

190   **HAM.** It is but foolery, but is such a kind of gaingiving° as would perhaps trouble a woman.

      HOR. If your mind dislike anything, obey it. I will forestall their repair hither, and say you are not fit.

      HAM. Not a whit, we defy augury. There is special providence in
195   the fall of a sparrow. If it be now, 'tis not to come; if it be not to come, it will be now; if it be not now, yet it will come. The readiness is all. Since no man of aught he leaves knows, what is't to leave betimes? Let be.

[*A table prepared. Enter* TRUMPETS, DRUMS, *and* OFFICERS *with cushions;* KING, QUEEN, OSRIC, *and all the* STATE, *with foils, daggers, and* LAERTES.]

      KING. Come, Hamlet, come, and take this hand from me.

[*The* KING *puts* LAERTES' *hand into* HAMLET'S.]

200   **HAM.** Give me your pardon, sir. I have done you wrong,
           But pardon 't as you are a gentleman.
           This presence knows, and you must needs have heard,
           How I am punished with a sore distraction.
           What I have done
205   That might your nature, honor, and exception,
           Roughly awake, I here proclaim was madness.
           Was 't Hamlet wronged Laertes? Never Hamlet.
           If Hamlet from himself be ta'en away,
           And when he's not himself does wrong Laertes,
210   Then Hamlet does it not, Hamlet denies it.
           Who does it then? His madness. If't be so,
           Hamlet is of the faction that is wronged;
           His madness is poor Hamlet's enemy.
           Sir, in this audience,
215   Let my disclaiming from a purposed evil
           Free me so far in your most generous thoughts
           That I have shot my arrow o'er the house
           And hurt my brother.

---

    190   **gaingiving** misgiving

LAER.   I am satisfied in nature,
Whose motive in this case should stir me most
220   To my revenge. But in my terms of honor
I stand aloof, and will no reconcilement
Till by some elder masters of known honor
I have a voice and precedent° of peace
To keep my name ungored. But till that time
225   I do receive your offered love like love,
And will not wrong it.

HAM.   I embrace it freely,
And will this brother's wager frankly play.
Give us the foils.

LAER.   Come, one for me.

HAM.   I'll be your foil,° Laertes. In mine ignorance
230   Your skill shall, like a star i' th' darkest night,
Stick fiery off indeed.

LAER.   You mock me, sir.

HAM.   No, by this hand.

KING.   Give them the foils, young Osric. Cousin Hamlet,
You know the wager?

HAM.   Very well, my lord:
235   Your Grace has laid the odds o' th' weaker side.

KING.   I do not fear it, I have seen you both;
But since he is bettered,° we have therefore odds.

LAER.   This is too heavy; let me see another.

HAM.   This likes me well. These foils have all a length?°

[*They prepare to play.*]

240   **OSR.**   Ay, my good lord.

KING.   Set me the stoups of wine upon that table.
If Hamlet give the first or second hit,
Or quit in answer° of the third exchange,
Let all the battlements their ordnance fire.

---

223   **voice and precedent** authoritative statement justified by precedent
229   **foil** (1) setting for gem (2) weapon
237   **bettered** perfected through training
239   **have all a length** are all of the same length
243   **quit in answer** literally, give as good as he gets (i.e., if the third bout is a draw)

245   The king shall drink to Hamlet's better breath,
       And in the cup an union° shall he throw,
       Richer than that which four successive kings
       In Denmark's crown have worn. Give me the cups,
       And let the kettle to the trumpet speak,
250   The trumpet to the cannoneer without,
       The cannons to the heavens, the heaven to earth,
       'Now the king drinks to Hamlet'. Come, begin—

[Trumpets the while.]

       And you, the judges, bear a wary eye.

HAM. Come on, sir.

LAER.   Come, my lord.

[They play.]

HAM.   One.

LAER.   No.

HAM.   Judgment.

255 **OSR.** A hit, a very palpable hit.

[Drums, trumpets, and shot. Flourish; a piece goes off.]

LAER. Well, again.

KING. Stay, give me drink. Hamlet, this pearl is thine.
       Here's to they health. Give him the cup.

HAM. I'll play this bout first; set it by awhile.
260   Come.

[They play.]

       Another hit; what say you?

LAER. I do confess't.

KING. Our son shall win.

QUEEN.   He's fat,° and scant of breath.
       Here, Hamlet, take my napkin, rub thy brows.
265   The queen carouses to thy fortune, Hamlet.

HAM. Good madam!

KING. Gertrude, do not drink.

QUEEN. I will, my lord; I pray you pardon me.

---

246   **union** pearl
263   **fat** out of training

KING. [*Aside.*] It is the poisoned cup; it is too late.

270 HAM. I dare not drink yet, madam; by and by.

QUEEN. Come, let me wipe thy face.

LAER. My lord, I'll hit him now.

KING.   I do not think't.

LAER. [*Aside.*] And yet it is almost against my conscience.

HAM. Come, for the third, Laertes. You do but dally.
275 I pray you pass with your best violence;
I am afeard you make a wanton of me.°

LAER. Say you so? Come on.

[*They play.*]

OSR. Nothing, neither way.

LAER. Have at you now!

[*LAERTES wounds HAMLET; then, in scuffling, they change rapiers.*]

280 KING. Part them. They are incensed.

HAM. Nay, come again.

[*HAMLET wounds LAERTES. The QUEEN falls.*]

OSR. Look to the queen there, ho!

HOR. They bleed on both sides. How is it, my lord?

OSR. How is't, Laertes?

285 LAER. Why, as a woodcock to mine own springe,° Osric.
I am justly killed with mine own treachery.

HAM. How does the queen?

KING.   She swoons to see them bleed.

QUEEN. No, no, the drink, the drink! O my dear Hamlet!
The drink, the drink! I am poisoned. [*Dies.*]

290 HAM. O, villainy! Ho! let the door be locked.
Treachery! seek it out.

[*LAERTES falls. Exit OSRIC.*]

LAER. It is here, Hamlet. Hamlet, thou art slain;
No med'cine in the world can do thee good.

---

276   **make a wanton of me** trifle with me
285   **springe** trap

In thee there is not half an hour's life.
295 The treacherous instrument is in thy hand,
Unbated° and envenomed. The foul practice°
Hath turned itself on me. Lo, here I lie,
Never to rise again. Thy mother's poisoned.
I can no more. The king, the king's to blame.

300 **HAM.** The point envenomed too?
Then, venom, to thy work. [*Wounds the* KING.]

ALL. Treason! treason!

KING. O, yet defend me, friends. I am but hurt.

HAM. Here, thou incestuous, murd'rous damnéd Dane,
305 Drink off this potion. Is thy union here?
Follow my mother. [KING *dies.*]

LAER.   He is justly served.
It is a poison tempered by himself.
Exchange forgiveness with me, noble Hamlet.
Mine and my father's death come not upon thee,
310 Nor thine on me! [*Dies.*]

HAM. Heaven make thee free of it! I follow thee.
I am dead, Horatio. Wretched queen, adieu!
You that look pale and tremble at this chance,
That are but mutes or audience to this act,
315 Had I but time, as this fell° sergeant° Death
Is strict in his arrest, O, I could tell you—
But let it be. Horatio, I am dead:
Thou livest; report me and my cause aright
To the unsatisfied.

HOR.   Never believe it.
320 I am more an antique Roman than a Dane.
Here's yet some liquor left.

HAM.   As th'art a man,
Give me the cup. Let go. By heaven, I'll ha't.
O God, Horatio, what a wounded name,
Things standing thus unknown, shall I leave behind me!
325 If thou didst ever hold me in thy heart,

---

296 **Unbated** unblunted
practice plot
315 **fell** cruel
sergeant an officer whose duty is to summon persons to appear before a court

Absent thee from felicity awhile,
And in this harsh world draw thy breath in pain,
To tell my story.

[*A march afar off.*]

What warlike noise is this?

[*Enter* OSRIC.]

OSR. Young Fortinbras, with conquest come from Poland,
330   To th' ambassadors of England gives
This warlike volley.

HAM.   O, I die, Horatio!
The potent poison quite o'er-crows° my spirit.
I cannot live to hear the news from England,
But I do prophesy th' election lights
335   On Fortinbras. He has my dying voice.°
So tell him, with th' occurrents, more and less,°
Which have solicited°—the rest is silence. [*Dies.*]

HOR. Now cracks a noble heart. Good night, sweet prince,
And flights of angels sing thee to thy rest! [*March within.*]
340   Why does the drum come hither?

[*Enter* FORTINBRAS, *with the* AMBASSADORS *and with drum, colors, and*
ATTENDANTS.]

FORT. Where is this sight?

HOR.   What is it you would see?
If aught of woe or wonder, cease your search.

FORT. This quarry° cries on havoc. O proud death,
What feast is toward° in thine eternal cell
345   That thou so many princes at a shot
So bloodily hast struck?

AMB.   The sight is dismal;
And our affairs from England come too late.

---

332   **o'er-crows** triumphs over
335   **voice** vote
336   **more and less** great and small
337   **solicited** incited, prompted
343   **quarry** pile of dead
344   **toward** impending

The ears are senseless that should give us hearing
To tell him his commandment is fulfilled,
350 That Rosencrantz and Guildenstern are dead.
Where should we have our thanks?

HOR.   Not from his mouth,
Had it th' ability of life to thank you.
He never gave commandment for their death.
But since, so jump° upon this bloody question,
355 You from the Polack wars, and you from England,
Are here arrived, give order that these bodies
High on a stage be placéd to the view,
And let me speak to th' yet unknowing world
How these things came about. So shall you hear
360 Of carnal, bloody, and unnatural acts;
Of accidental judgments, casual slaughters;
Of deaths put on° by cunning and forced cause;°
And, in this upshot, purposes mistook
Fall'n on th' inventors' heads. All this can I
365 Truly deliver.

FORT.   Let us haste to hear it,
And call the noblest to the audience.
For me, with sorrow I embrace my fortune.
I have some rights of memory in this kingdom,
Which now to claim my vantage doth invite me.

370 HOR. Of that I shall have also cause to speak,
And from his mouth whose voice will draw on more.
But let this same be presently performed,
Even while men's minds are wild, lest more mischance
On plots and errors happen.

FORT.   Let four captains
375 Bear Hamlet like a soldier to the stage,
For he was likely, had he been put on,°
To have proved most royal; and for his passage°
The soldier's music and the rite of war

---

354 **jump** exactly
362 **put on** instigated
      forced cause by reason of compulsion
376 **put on** set to perform in office
377 **passage** death

Speak loudly for him.

380 Take up the bodies. Such a sight as this
Becomes the field, but here shows much amiss.
Go, bid the soldiers shoot.

[*Exeunt marching. A peal of ordnance shot off.*]

Related Readings

| Bharati Mukherjee | # The Management of Grief |

In the following story, a mother is forced to come to terms with her grief when she loses her family in a plane crash.

A WOMAN I DON'T KNOW is boiling tea the Indian way in my kitchen. There are a lot of women I don't know in my kitchen, whispering, and moving tactfully. They open doors, rummage through the pantry, and try not to ask me where things are kept. They remind me of when my sons were small, on Mother's Day or when Vikram and I were tired, and they would make big, sloppy omelets. I would lie in bed pretending I didn't hear them.

Dr. Sharma, the treasurer of the Indo-Canada Society, pulls me into the hallway. He wants to know if I am worried about money. His wife, who has just come up from the basement with a tray of empty cups and glasses, scolds him. "Don't bother Mrs. Bhave with mundane details." She looks so monstrously pregnant her baby must be days overdue. I tell her she shouldn't be carrying heavy things. "Shaila," she says, smiling, "this is the fifth." Then she grabs a teenager by his shirttails. He slips his Walkman off his head. He has to be one of her four children, they have the same domed and dented foreheads. "What's the official word now?" she demands. The boy slips his headphones back on. "They're acting evasive, Ma. They're saying it could be an accident or a terrorist bomb."

All morning, the boys have been muttering, Sikh[1] Bomb, Sikh Bomb. The men, not using the word, bow their heads in agreement. Mrs. Sharma touches her forehead at such a word. At least they've stopped talking about space debris and Russian lasers.

Two radios are going in the dining room. They are tuned to different stations. Someone must have brought the radios down from my boys' bedrooms. I haven't gone into their rooms since Kusum came running across

---

1. **Sikh** follower of a religion that is a combination of the Muslim faith and Hinduism. The Sikh desire for independence from the rest of the Indian population has led to much violence in India—thus the fear of a "Sikh Bomb."

the front lawn in her bathrobe. She looked so funny, I was laughing when I opened the door.

The big TV in the den is being whizzed through American networks and cable channels.

"Damn!" some man swears bitterly. "How can these preachers carry on like nothing's happened?" I want to tell him we're not that important. You look at the audience, and at the preacher in his blue robe with his beautiful white hair, the potted palm trees under a blue sky, and you know they care about nothing.

The phone rings and rings. Dr. Sharma's taken charge. "We're with her," he keeps saying. "Yes, yes, the doctor has given calming pills. Yes, yes, pills are having necessary effect." I wonder if pills alone explain this calm. Not peace, just a deadening quiet. I was always controlled, but never repressed. Sound can reach me, but my body is tensed, ready to scream. I hear their voices all around me. I hear my boys and Vikram cry, "Mommy, Shaila!" and their screams insulate me, like headphones.

The woman boiling water tells her story again and again. "I got the news first. My cousin called from Halifax before six A.M., can you imagine? He'd gotten up for prayers and his son was studying for medical exams and he heard on a rock channel that something had happened to a plane. They said first it had disappeared from the radar, like a giant eraser just reached out. His father called me, so I said to him, what do you mean, 'something bad'? You mean a hijacking? And he said, *behn*, there is no confirmation of any-thing yet, but check with your neighbors because a lot of them must be on the plane. So I called poor Kusum straightaway. I knew Kusum's husband and daughter were booked to go yesterday."

Kusum lives across the street from me. She and Satish had moved in less than a month ago. They said they needed a bigger place. All these people, the Sharmas and friends from the Indo-Canada Society had been there for the housewarming. Satish and Kusum made homemade tandoori on their big gas grill and even the white neighbors piled their plates high with that luridly red, charred, juicy chicken. Their younger daughter had danced, and even our boys had broken away from the Stanley Cup telecast to put in a reluctant appearance. Everyone took pictures for their albums and for the community newspapers—another of our families had made it big in Toronto—and now I wonder how many of those happy faces are gone. "Why does God give us so much if all along He intends to take it away?" Kusum asks me.

I nod. We sit on carpeted stairs, holding hands like children. "I never once told him that I loved him," I say. I was too much the well brought up woman. I was so well brought up I never felt comfortable calling my hus-band by his first name.

"It's all right," Kusum says. "He knew. My husband knew. They felt it.

Modern young girls have to say it because what they feel is fake."

Kusum's daughter, Pam, runs in with an overnight case. Pam's in her McDonald's uniform. "Mummy! You have to get dressed!" Panic makes her cranky. "A reporter's on his way here."

"Why?"

"You want to talk to him in your bathrobe?" She starts to brush her mother's long hair. She's the daughter who is always in trouble. She dates Canadian boys and hangs out in the mall, shopping for tight sweaters. The younger one, the goody-goody one according to Pam, the one with a voice so sweet that when she sang *bhajans*[2] for Ethiopian relief even a frugal man like my husband wrote out a hundred dollar check, *she* was on that plane. *She* was going to spend July and August with grandparents because Pam wouldn't go. Pam said she'd rather waitress at McDonald's. "If it's a choice between Bombay and Wonderland, I'm picking Wonderland," she'd said.

"Leave me alone," Kusum yells. "You know what I want to do? If I didn't have to look after you now, I'd hang myself."

Pam's young face goes blotchy with pain. "Thanks," she says, "don't let me stop you."

"Hush," pregnant Mrs. Sharma scolds Pam. "Leave your mother alone. Mr. Sharma will tackle the reporters and fill out the forms. He'll say what has to be said."

Pam stands her ground. "You think I don't know what Mummy's thinking? *Why her?* that's what. That's sick! Mummy wishes my little sister were alive and I were dead."

Kusum's hand in mine is trembly hot. We continue to sit on the stairs.

She calls before she arrives, wondering if there's anything I need. Her name is Judith Templeton and she's an appointee of the provincial government. "Multiculturalism?" I ask, and she says "partially," but that her mandate is bigger. "I've been told you knew many of the people on the flight," she says. "Perhaps if you'd agree to help us reach the others . . . ?"

She gives me time at least to put on tea water and pick up the mess in the front room. I have a few *samosas* from Kusum's housewarming that I could fry up, but then I think, why prolong this visit?

Judith Templeton is much younger than she sounded. She wears a blue suit with a white blouse and a polka dot tie. Her blond hair is cut short, her only jewelry is pearl drop earrings. Her briefcase is new and expensive looking, a gleaming cordovan leather. She sits with it across her lap. When she

---

2. *bhajans* hymns

looks out the front windows onto the street, her contact lenses seem to float in front of her light blue eyes.

"What sort of help do you want from me?" I ask. She has refused the tea, out of politeness, but I insist, along with some slightly stale biscuits.

"I have no experience," she admits. "That is, I have an MSW and I've worked in liaison with accident victims, but I mean I have no experience with a tragedy of this scale—"

"Who could?" I ask.

"—and with the complications of culture, language, and customs. Someone mentioned that Mrs. Bhave is a pillar—because you've taken it more calmly."

At this, perhaps, I frown, for she reaches forward, almost to take my hand. "I hope you understand my meaning, Mrs. Bhave. There are hundreds of people in Metro directly affected, like you, and some of them speak no English. There are some widows who've never handled money or gone on a bus, and there are old parents who still haven't eaten or gone outside their bedrooms. Some houses and apartments have been looted. Some wives are still hysterical. Some husbands are in shock and profound depression. We want to help, but our hands are tied in so many ways. We have to distribute money to some people, and there are legal documents—these things can be done. We have interpreters, but we don't always have the human touch, or maybe the right human touch. We don't want to make mistakes, Mrs. Bhave, and that's why we'd like to ask you to help us."

"More mistakes, you mean," I say.

"Police matters are not in my hands," she answers.

"Nothing I can do will make any difference," I say. "We must all grieve in our own way."

"But you are coping very well. All the people said, Mrs. Bhave is the strongest person of all. Perhaps if the others could see you, talk with you, it would help them."

"By the standards of the people you call hysterical, I am behaving very oddly and very badly, Miss Templeton." I want to say to her, *I wish I could scream, starve, walk into Lake Ontario, jump from a bridge.* "They would not see me as a model. I do not see myself as a model."

I am a freak. No one who has ever known me would think of me reacting this way. This terrible calm will not go away.

She asks me if she may call again, after I get back from a long trip that we all must make. "Of course," I say. "Feel free to call, anytime."

Four days later, I find Kusum squatting on a rock overlooking a bay in Ireland. It isn't a big rock, but it juts sharply out over water. This is as close as we'll ever get to them. June breezes balloon out her sari and unpin her knee-length hair. She has the bewildered look of a sea creature whom the tides have stranded.

It's been one hundred hours since Kusum came stumbling and screaming across my lawn. Waiting around the hospital, we've heard many stories. The police, the diplomats, they tell us things thinking that we're strong, that knowledge is helpful to the grieving, and maybe it is. Some, I know, prefer ignorance, or their own versions. The plane broke into two, they say. Unconsciousness was instantaneous. No one suffered. My boys must have just finished their breakfasts. They loved eating on planes, they loved the smallness of plates, knives, and forks. Last year they saved the airline salt and pepper shakers. Half an hour more and they would have made it to Heathrow.

Kusum says that we can't escape our fate. She says that all those people— our husbands, my boys, her girl with the nightingale voice, all those Hindus, Christians, Sikhs, Muslims, Parsis,[3] and atheists on that plane—were fated to die together off this beautiful bay. She learned this from a swami[4] in Toronto.

I have my valium.

Six of us "relatives"—two widows and four widowers—choose to spend the day today by the waters instead of sitting in a hospital room and scanning photographs of the dead. That's what they call us now: relatives. I've looked through twenty-seven photos in two days. They're very kind to us, the Irish are very understanding. Sometimes understanding means freeing a tourist bus for this trip to the bay, so we can pretend to spy our loved ones through the glassiness of waves or in sun-speckled cloud shapes.

I could die here, too, and be content.

"What is that, out there?" She's standing and flapping her hands and for a moment I see a head shape bobbing in the waves. She's standing in the water, I, on the boulder. The tide is low, and a round, black, head-sized rock has just risen from the waves. She returns, her sari end dripping and ruined and her face is a twisted remnant of hope, the way mine was a hundred hours ago, still laughing but inwardly knowing that nothing but the ultimate tragedy could bring two women together at six o'clock on a Sunday morning. I watch her face sag into blankness.

"That water felt warm, Shaila," she says at length.

"You can't," I say. "We have to wait for our turn to come."

I haven't eaten in four days, haven't brushed my teeth.

"I know," she says. "I tell myself I have no right to grieve. They are in a better place than we are. My swami says I should be thrilled for them. My swami says depression is a sign of our selfishness."

---

3. **Parsis** Indians descended from Persian refugees who fled—mostly to Bombay—in the seventeenth century

4. **swami** Hindu religious teacher or monk

Maybe I'm selfish. Selfishly I break away from Kusum and run, sandals slapping against stones, to the water's edge. What if my boys aren't lying pinned under the debris? What if they aren't stuck a mile below that innocent blue chop? What if, given the strong currents. . . .

Now I've ruined my sari, one of my best. Kusum has joined me, knee-deep in water that feels to me like a swimming pool. I could settle in the water, and my husband would take my hand and the boys would slap water in my face just to see me scream.

"Do you remember what good swimmers my boys were, Kusum?"

"I saw the medals," she says.

One of the widowers, Dr. Ranganathan from Montreal, walks out to us, carrying his shoes in one hand. He's an electrical engineer. Someone at the hotel mentioned his work is famous around the world, something about the place where physics and electricity come together. He has lost a huge family, something indescribable. "With some luck," Dr. Ranganathan suggests to me, "a good swimmer could make it safely to some island. It is quite possible that there may be many, many microscopic islets scattered around."

"You're not just saying that?" I tell Dr. Ranganathan about Vinod, my elder son. Last year he took diving as well.

"It's a parent's duty to hope," he says. "It is foolish to rule out possibilities that have not been tested. I myself have not surrendered hope."

Kusum is sobbing once again. "Dear lady," he says, laying his free hand on her arm, and she calms down.

"Vinod is how old?" he asks me. He's very careful, as we all are. *Is*, not was.

"Fourteen. Yesterday he was fourteen. His father and uncle were going to take him down to the Taj and give him a big birthday party. I couldn't go with them because I couldn't get two weeks off from my stupid job in June." I process bills for a travel agent. June is a big travel month.

Dr. Ranganathan whips the pockets of his suit jacket inside out. Squashed roses, in darkening shades of pink, float on the water. He tore the roses off creepers in somebody's garden. He didn't ask anyone if he could pluck the roses, but now there's been an article about it in the local papers. When you see an Indian person, it says, please give him or her flowers.

"A strong youth of fourteen," he says, "can very likely pull to safety a younger one."

My sons, though four years apart, were very close. Vinod wouldn't let Mithun drown. *Electrical engineering*, I think, foolishly perhaps: this man knows important secrets of the universe, things closed to me. Relief spins me lightheaded. No wonder my boys' photographs haven't turned up in the gallery of photos of the recovered dead. "Such pretty roses," I say.

"My wife loved pink roses. Every Friday I had to bring a bunch home. I used to say, why? After twenty odd years of marriage you're still needing proof positive of my love?" He has identified his wife and three of his children. Then others from Montreal, the lucky ones, intact families with no survivors. He chuckles as he wades back to shore. Then he swings around to ask me a question. "Mrs. Bhave, you are wanting to throw in some roses for your loved ones? I have two big ones left."

But I have other things to float: Vinod's pocket calculator; a half-painted model B-52 for my Mithun. They'd want them on their island. And for my husband? For him I let fall into the calm, glassy waters a poem I wrote in the hospital yesterday. Finally he'll know my feelings for him.

"Don't tumble, the rocks are slippery," Dr. Ranganathan cautions. He holds out a hand for me to grab.

Then it's time to get back on the bus, time to rush back to our waiting posts on hospital benches.

Kusum is one of the lucky ones. The lucky ones flew here, identified in multiplicate their loved ones, then will fly to India with the bodies for proper ceremonies. Satish is one of the few males who surfaced. The photos of faces we saw on the walls in an office at Heathrow and here in the hospital are mostly of women. Women have more body fat, a nun said to me matter-of-factly. They float better.

Today I was stopped by a young sailor on the street. He had loaded bodies, he'd gone into the water when—he checks my face for signs of strength—when the sharks were first spotted. I don't blush, and he breaks down. "It's all right," I say. "Thank you." I had heard about the sharks from Dr. Ranganathan. In his orderly mind, science brings understanding, it holds no terror. It is the shark's duty. For every deer there is a hunter, for every fish a fisherman.

The Irish are not shy; they rush to me and give me hugs and some are crying. I cannot imagine reactions like that on the streets of Toronto. Just strangers, and I am touched. Some carry flowers with them and give them to any Indian they see.

After lunch, a policeman I have gotten to know quite well catches hold of me. He says he thinks he has a match for Vinod. I explain what a good swimmer Vinod is.

"You want me with you when you look at photos?" Dr. Ranganathan walks ahead of me into the picture gallery. In these matters, he is a scientist, and I am grateful. It is a new perspective. "They have performed miracles," he says. "We are indebted to them."

The first day or two the policemen showed us relatives only one picture at a time; now they're in a hurry, they're eager to lay out the possibles, and even the probables.

The face on the photo is of a boy much like Vinod; the same intelligent eyes, the same thick brows dipping into a V. But this boy's features, even his cheeks, are puffier, wider, mushier.

"No." My gaze is pulled by other pictures. There are five other boys who look like Vinod.

The nun assigned to console me rubs the first picture with a fingertip. "When they've been in the water for a while, love, they look a little heavier." The bones under the skin are broken, they said on the first day—try to adjust your memories. It's important.

"It's not him. I'm his mother. I'd know."

"I know this one!" Dr. Ranganathan cries out suddenly from the back of the gallery. "And this one!" I think he senses that I don't want to find my boys. "They are the Kutty brothers. They were also from Montreal." I don't mean to be crying. On the contrary, I am ecstatic. My suitcase in the hotel is packed heavy with dry clothes for my boys.

The policeman starts to cry. "I am so sorry, I am so sorry, ma'am. I really thought we had a match."

With the nun ahead of us and the policeman behind, we, the unlucky ones without our children's bodies, file out of the makeshift gallery.

From Ireland most of us go to India. Kusum and I take the same direct flight to Bombay, so I can help her clear customs quickly. But we have to argue with a man in uniform. He has large boils on his face. The boils swell and glow with sweat as we argue with him. He wants Kusum to wait in line and he refuses to take authority because his boss is on a tea break. But Kusum won't let her coffins out of sight, and I shan't desert her though I know my parents, elderly and diabetic, must be waiting in a stuffy car in a scorching lot.

"You bastard!" I scream at the man with the popping boils. Other passengers press closer. "You think we're smuggling contraband in those coffins!"

Once upon a time we were well brought up women; we were dutiful wives who kept our heads veiled, our voices shy and sweet.

In India, I become, once again, an only child of rich, ailing parents. Old friends of the family come to pay their respects. Some are Sikh, and inwardly, involuntarily, I cringe. My parents are progressive people; they do not blame communities for a few individuals.

In Canada it is a different story now.

"Stay longer," my mother pleads. "Canada is a cold place. Why would you want to be all by yourself?" I stay.

Three months pass. Then another.

"Vikram wouldn't have wanted you to give up things!" they protest.

They call my husband by the name he was born with. In Toronto he'd changed to Vik so the men he worked with at his office would find his name as easy as Rod or Chris. "You know, the dead aren't cut off from us!"

My grandmother, the spoiled daughter of a rich *zamindar*,[5] shaved her head with rusty razor blades when she was widowed at sixteen. My grandfather died of childhood diabetes when he was nineteen, and she saw herself as the harbinger of bad luck. My mother grew up without parents, raised indifferently by an uncle, while her true mother slept in a hut behind the main estate house and took her food with the servants. She grew up a rationalist.[6] My parents abhor mindless mortification.

The zamindar's daughter kept stubborn faith in Vedic[7] rituals; my parents rebelled. I am trapped between two modes of knowledge. At thirty-six, I am too old to start over and too young to give up. Like my husband's spirit, I flutter between worlds.

Courting aphasia,[8] we travel. We travel with our phalanx of servants and poor relatives. To hill stations and to beach resorts. We play contract bridge in dusty gymkhana clubs. We ride stubby ponies up crumbly mountain trails. At tea dances, we let ourselves be twirled twice round the ballroom. We hit the holy spots we hadn't made time for before. In Varanasi, Kalighat, Rishikesh, Hardwar, astrologers and palmists seek me out and for a fee offer me cosmic consolations.

Already the widowers among us are being shown new bride candidates. They cannot resist the call of custom, the authority of their parents and older brothers. They must marry; it is the duty of a man to look after a wife. The new wives will be young widows with children, destitute but of good family. They will make loving wives, but the men will shun them. I've had calls from the men over crackling Indian telephone lines. "Save me," they say, these substantial, educated, successful men of forty. "My parents are arranging a marriage for me." In a month they will have buried one family and returned to Canada with a new bride and partial family.

I am comparatively lucky. No one here thinks of arranging a husband for an unlucky widow.

Then, on the third day of the sixth month into this odyssey, in an abandoned temple in a tiny Himalayan village, as I make my offering of flowers

---

5. *zamindar* landlord who collects revenues from farmers to give to the government of India
6. **rationalist** someone who believes that religion has no basis in reason and emphasizes reason over experience and emotions
7. **Vedic** of or related to the ancient sacred writing of the Hindus called the Vedas; the period and culture they represent
8. **aphasia** inability to use language

and sweetmeats to the god of a tribe of animists,[9] my husband descends to me. He is squatting next to a scrawny *sadhu*[10] in moth-eaten robes. Vikram wears the vanilla suit he wore the last time I hugged him. The *sadhu* tosses petals on a butter-fed flame, reciting Sanskrit[11] mantras and sweeps his face of flies. My husband takes my hands in his.

You're beautiful, he starts. Then, *What are you doing here?*

Shall I stay? I ask. He only smiles, but already the image is fading. *You must finish alone what we started together.* No seaweed wreathes his mouth. He speaks too fast just as he used to when we were an envied family in our pink split-level. He is gone.

In the windowless altar room, smoky with joss sticks and clarified butter lamps, a sweaty hand gropes for my blouse. I do not shriek. The *sadhu* arranges his robe. The lamps hiss and sputter out.

When we come out of the temple, my mother says, "Did you feel something weird in there?"

My mother has no patience with ghosts, prophetic dreams, holy men, and cults.

"No," I lie. "Nothing."

But she knows that she's lost me. She knows that in days I shall be leaving.

Kusum's put her house up for sale. She wants to live in an ashram[12] in Hardwar. Moving to Hardwar was her swami's idea. Her swami runs two ashrams, the one in Hardwar and another here in Toronto.

"Don't run away," I tell her.

"I'm not running away," she says. "I'm pursuing inner peace. You think you or that Ranganathan fellow are better off?"

Pam's left for California. She wants to do some modelling, she says. She says when she comes into her share of the insurance money she'll open a yoga-cum-aerobics studio in Hollywood. She sends me postcards so naughty I daren't leave them on the coffee table. Her mother has withdrawn from her and the world.

The rest of us don't lose touch, that's the point. Talk is all we have, says Dr. Ranganathan, who has also resisted his relatives and returned to Montreal and to his job, alone. He says, whom better to talk with than other relatives? We've been melted down and recast as a new tribe.

---

9. **animists** people who believe in spiritual beings apart from natural bodies
10. *sadhu* Hindu holy man
11. **Sanskrit** ancient language of India and Hinduism
12. **ashram** religious retreat

He calls me twice a week from Montreal. Every Wednesday night and every Saturday afternoon. He is changing jobs, going to Ottawa. But Ottawa is over a hundred miles away, and he is forced to drive two hundred and twenty miles a day. He can't bring himself to sell his house. The house is a temple, he says; the king-sized bed in the master bedroom is a shrine. He sleeps on a folding cot. A devotee.

There are still some hysterical relatives. Judith Templeton's list of those needing help and those who've "accepted" is in nearly perfect balance. Acceptance means you speak of your family in the past tense and you make active plans for moving ahead with your life. There are courses at Seneca and Ryerson we could be taking. Her gleaming leather briefcase is full of college catalogues and lists of cultural societies that need our help. She has done impressive work, I tell her.

"In the textbooks on grief management," she replies—I am her confidante, I realize, one of the few whose grief has not sprung bizarre obsessions—"there are stages to pass through: rejection, depression, acceptance, reconstruction." She has compiled a chart and finds that six months after the tragedy, none of us still reject reality, but only a handful are reconstructing. "Depressed Acceptance" is the plateau we've reached. Remarriage is a major step in reconstruction (though she's a little surprised, even shocked, over *how* quickly some of the men have taken on new families). Selling one's house and changing jobs and cities is healthy.

How do I tell Judith Templeton that my family surrounds me, and that like creatures in epics, they've changed shapes? She sees me as calm and accepting but worries that I have no job, no career. My closest friends are worse off than I. I cannot tell her my days, even my nights, are thrilling.

She asks me to help with families she can't reach at all. An elderly couple in Agincourt whose sons were killed just weeks after they had brought their parents over from a village in Punjab. From their names, I know they are Sikh. Judith Templeton and a translator have visited them twice with offers of money for air fare to Ireland, with bank forms, power-of-attorney forms, but they have refused to sign, or to leave their tiny apartment. Their sons' money is frozen in the bank. Their sons' investment apartments have been trashed by tenants, the furnishings sold off. The parents fear that anything they sign or any money they receive will end the company's or the country's obligations to them. They fear they are selling their sons for two airline tickets to a place they've never seen.

The high-rise apartment is a tower of Indians and West Indians, with a sprinkling of Orientals. The nearest bus stop kiosk is lined with women in saris. Boys practice cricket in the parking lot. Inside the building, even I wince a bit from the ferocity of onion fumes, the distinctive and immediate

Indianness of frying *ghee*,[13] but Judith Templeton maintains a steady flow of information. These poor old people are in imminent danger of losing their place and all their services.

I say to her, "They are Sikh. They will not open up to a Hindu woman." And what I want to add is, as much as I try not to, I stiffen now at the sight of beards and turbans. I remember a time when we all trusted each other in this new country, it was only the new country we worried about.

The two rooms are dark and stuffy. The lights are off, and an oil lamp sputters on the coffee table. The bent old lady has let us in, and her husband is wrapping a white turban over his oiled, hip-length hair. She immediately goes to the kitchen, and I hear the most familiar sound of an Indian home, tap water hitting and filling a teapot.

They have not paid their utility bills, out of fear and the inability to write a check. The telephone is gone; electricity and gas and water are soon to follow. They have told Judith their sons will provide. They are good boys, and they have always earned and looked after their parents.

We converse a bit in Hindi. They do not ask about the crash and I wonder if I should bring it up. If they think I am here merely as a translator, then they may feel insulted. There are thousands of Punjabi-speakers, Sikhs, in Toronto to do a better job. And so I say to the old lady, "I too have lost my sons, and my husband, in the crash."

Her eyes immediately fill with tears. The man mutters a few words which sound like a blessing. "God provides and God takes away," he says.

I want to say, but only men destroy and give back nothing. "My boys and my husband are not coming back," I say. "We have to understand that."

Now the old woman responds. "But who is to say? Man alone does not decide these things." To this her husband adds his agreement.

Judith asks about the bank papers, the release forms. With a stroke of a pen, they will have a provincial trustee to pay their bills, invest their money, send them a monthly pension.

"Do you know this woman?" I ask them.

The man raises his hand from the table, turns it over and seems to regard each finger separately before he answers. "This young lady is always coming here, we make tea for her and she leaves papers for us to sign." His eyes scan a pile of papers in the corner of the room. "Soon we will be out of tea, then will she go away?"

The old lady adds, "I have asked my neighbors and no one else gets *angrezi*[14] visitors. What have we done?"

---

13. *ghee* butter made from buffalo milk
14. *angrezi* English

"It's her job," I try to explain. "The government is worried. Soon you will have no place to stay, no lights, no gas, no water."

"Government will get its money. Tell her not to worry, we are honorable people."

I try to explain the government wishes to give money, not take. He raises his hand. "Let them take," he says. "We are accustomed to that. That is no problem."

"We are strong people," says the wife. "Tell her that."

"Who needs all this machinery?" demands the husband. "It is unhealthy, the bright lights, the cold air on a hot day, the cold food, the four gas rings. God will provide, not government."

"When our boys return," the mother says. Her husband sucks his teeth. "Enough talk," he says.

Judith breaks in. "Have you convinced them?" The snaps on her cordovan briefcase go off like firecrackers in that quiet apartment. She lays the sheaf of legal papers on the coffee table. "If they can't write their names, an X will do—I've told them that."

Now the old lady has shuffled to the kitchen and soon emerges with a pot of tea and two cups. "I think my bladder will go first on a job like this," Judith says to me, smiling. "If only there was some way of reaching them. Please thank her for the tea. Tell her she's very kind."

I nod in Judith's direction and tell them in Hindi, "She thanks you for the tea. She thinks you are being very hospitable but she doesn't have the slightest idea what it means."

I want to say, humor her. I want to say, my boys and my husband are with me too, more than ever. I look in the old man's eyes and I can read his stubborn, peasant's message: *I have protected this woman as best I can. She is the only person I have left. Give to me or take from me what you will, but I will not sign for it. I will not pretend that I can accept.*

In the car, Judith says, "You see what I'm up against? I'm sure they're lovely people, but their stubbornness and ignorance are driving me crazy. They think signing a paper is signing their sons' death warrants, don't they?"

I am looking out the window. I want to say, *In our culture, it is a parent's duty to hope.*

"Now Shaila, this next woman is a real mess. She cries day and night, and she refuses all medical help. We may have to—"

"—Let me out at the subway," I say.

"I beg your pardon?" I can feel those blue eyes staring at me.

It would not be like her to disobey. She merely disapproves, and slows at a corner to let me out. Her voice is plaintive. "Is there anything I said? Anything I did?"

I could answer her suddenly in a dozen ways, but I choose not to. "Shaila? Let's talk about it," I hear, then slam the door.

A wife and mother begins her new life in a new country, and that life is cut short. Yet her husband tells her: Complete what we have started. We, who stayed out of politics and came halfway around the world to avoid religious and political feuding have been the first in the New World to die from it. I no longer know what we started, nor how to complete it. I write letters to the editors of local papers and to members of Parliament. Now at least they admit it was a bomb. One MP answers back, with sympathy, but with a challenge. You want to make a difference? Work on a campaign. Work on mine. Politicize the Indian voter.

My husband's old lawyer helps me set up a trust. Vikram was a saver and a careful investor. He had saved the boys' boarding school and college fees. I sell the pink house at four times what we paid for it and take a small apartment downtown. I am looking for a charity to support.

We are deep in the Toronto winter, gray skies, icy pavements. I stay indoors, watching television. I have tried to assess my situation, how best to live my life, to complete what we began so many years ago. Kusum has written me from Hardwar that her life is now serene. She has seen Satish and has heard her daughter sing again. Kusum was on a pilgrimage, passing through a village when she heard a young girl's voice, singing one of her daughter's favorite *bhajans*. She followed the music through the squalor of a Himalayan village, to a hut where a young girl, an exact replica of her daughter, was fanning coals under the kitchen fire. When she appeared, the girl cried out, "Ma!" and ran away. What did I think of that?

I think I can only envy her.

Pam didn't make it to California, but writes me from Vancouver. She works in a department store, giving make-up hints to Indian and Oriental girls. Dr. Ranganathan has given up his commute, given up his house and job, and accepted an academic position in Texas where no one knows his story and he has vowed not to tell it. He calls me now once a week.

I wait, I listen, and I pray, but Vikram has not returned to me. The voices and the shapes and the nights filled with visions ended abruptly several weeks ago.

I take it as a sign.

One rare, beautiful, sunny day last week, returning from a small errand on Yonge Street, I was walking through the park from the subway to my apartment. I live equidistant from the Ontario Houses of Parliament and the university of Toronto. The day was not cold, but something in the bare trees caught my attention. I looked up from the gravel, into the branches and the clear blue sky beyond. I thought I heard the rustling of larger forms, and I waited a moment for voices. Nothing.

"What?" I asked.

Then as I stood in the path looking north to Queen's Park and west to the university, I heard the voices of my family one last time. *Your time has come*, they said. *Go, be brave.*

I do not know where this voyage I have begun will end. I do not know which direction I will take. I dropped the package on a park bench and started walking.

Of Revenge

Francis Bacon

Revenge is a key theme in Hamlet. *In this essay, Francis Bacon examines some of the motives for revenge. In the following reading,* The Embassy of Death: An Essay on Hamlet, *critic George Wilson Knight looks at Hamlet's obsession with revenge and how it corrupts his character.*

REVENGE IS A KIND of wild justice; which the more man's nature runs to, the more ought law to weed it out. For as for the first wrong, it doth but offend the law; but the revenge of that wrong putteth the law out of office. Certainly, in taking revenge, a man is but even with his enemy; but in passing it over, he is superior; for it is a prince's part to pardon. And Salomon, I am sure, saith, *It is the glory of a man to pass by an offence.* That which is past is gone, and irrevocable; and wise men have enough to do with things present and to come: therefore they do but trifle with themselves, that labour in past matters. There is no man doth a wrong for the wrong's sake; but thereby to purchase himself profit, or pleasure, or honour, or the like. Therefore why should I be angry with a man for loving himself better than me? And if any man should do wrong merely out of ill nature, why, yet it is but like the thorn or briar, which prick and scratch, because they can do no other. The most tolerable sort of revenge is for those wrongs which there is no law to remedy; but then let a man take heed the revenge be such as there is no law to punish; else a man's enemy is still beforehand, and it is two for one. Some, when they take revenge, are desirous the party should know whence it cometh: this is the more generous. For the delight seemeth to be not so much in doing the hurt as in making the party repent: but base and crafty cowards are like the arrow that flieth in the dark. Cosmus, duke of Florence, had a desperate saying against perfidious or neglecting friends, as if those wrongs were unpardonable: *You shall read* (saith he) *that we are commanded to forgive our enemies; but you never read that we are commanded to forgive our friends.* But yet the spirit of Job was in a better tune: *Shall we* (saith he) *take good at God's hands, and not be content to take evil also?* And so of friends in a proportion. This is certain, that a man that studieth revenge keeps his own wounds green, which otherwise would heal and do well. Public revenges are for the most part fortunate; as that for the death of Caesar; for the death of

Pertinax; for the death of Henry the Third of France; and many more. But in private revenges it is not so. Nay rather, vindicative persons live the life of witches; who as they are mischievous, so end they infortunate.

George Wilson Knight

The Embassy of Death: An Essay on *Hamlet*

IT IS USUAL in Shakespeare's plays for the main theme to be reflected in subsidiary[1] incidents, persons, and detailed suggestion throughout. Now the theme of *Hamlet* is death. Life that is bound for the disintegration of the grave, love that does not survive the loved one's life—both, in their insistence on death as the primary fact of nature, are branded on the mind of Hamlet, burned into it, searing it with agony. The bereavement of Hamlet and his consequent mental agony bordering on madness is mirrored in the bereavement of Ophelia and her madness. The death of the Queen's love is reflected in the swift passing of the love of the Player-Queen, in the 'Murder of Gonzago.' Death is over the whole play. Polonius and Ophelia die during the action, and Ophelia is buried before our eyes. Hamlet arranges the deaths of Rosencrantz and Guildenstern. The plot is set in motion by the murder of Hamlet's father, and the play opens with the apparition of the Ghost:

> What this may mean,
> *That thou, dead corse, again in complete steel*
> *Revisit'st thus the glimpses of the moon,*
> *Making night hideous; and we fools of nature*
> *So horridly to shake our dispositions*
> *With thoughts beyond the reaches of our souls?*　　　　(I.iv.51)

Those first scenes strike the note of the play—death. We hear of terrors beyond the grave, from the Ghost (I.v) and from the meditations of Hamlet (III.i). We hear of horrors in the grave from Hamlet whose mind is obsessed

---

1. **subsidiary** secondary; less important

with hideous thoughts of the body's decay. Hamlet's dialogue with the King about the dead Polonius (IV.iii.17) is painful; and the graveyard meditations, though often beautiful, are remorselessly realistic. Hamlet holds Yorick's skull:

> Hamlet. . . . *Now, get you to my lady's chamber and tell her, let her paint*
> *an inch thick, to this favour she must come; make her laugh at that.*
> *Prithee, Horatio, tell me one thing.*
> Horatio. *What's that, my lord?*
> Hamlet. *Dost thou think Alexander looked o' this fashion i' the earth?*
> Horatio. *E'en so.*
> Hamlet. *And smelt so? pah!*   (V.i.211)

The general thought of death, intimately related to the predominating human theme, the pain in Hamlet's mind, is thus suffused through the whole play. And yet the play, as a whole, scarcely gives us that sense of blackness and the abysms [2] of spiritual evil which we find in *Macbeth*; nor is there the universal gloom of *King Lear*. This is due partly to the difference in the technique of *Hamlet* from that of *Macbeth* or *King Lear*. Macbeth, the protagonist and heroic victim of evil, rises gigantic from the murk of an evil universe; Lear, the king of suffering, towers over a universe that itself toils in pain. Thus in *Macbeth* and *King Lear* the predominating imaginative atmospheres are used not to contrast with the mental universe of the hero, but to aid and support it, as it were, with similarity, to render realistic the extravagant and daring effects of volcanic passion to which the poet allows his protagonist to give voice. We are forced by the attendant personification, the verbal colour, the symbolism and events of the play as a whole, to feel the hero's suffering, to see with his eyes. But in *Hamlet* this is not so. We need not see through Hamlet's eyes. Though the idea of death is recurrent through the play, it is not implanted in the minds of other persons as is the consciousness of evil throughout *Macbeth* and the consciousness of suffering throughout *King Lear*. Except for the original murder of Hamlet's father, the *Hamlet* universe is one of healthy and robust life, good-nature, humour, romantic strength, and welfare: against this background is the figure of Hamlet pale with the consciousness of death. He is the ambassador of death walking amid life. The effect is at first primarily one of separation. But it is to be noted that the consciousness of death, and consequent bitterness, cruelty, and inaction, in Hamlet not only grows in his own mind disintegrating it as we watch, but also spreads its effects outward among the other persons

---

2. **abysms** the lowest depths

like a blighting disease, and, as the play progresses, by its very passivity and negation of purpose, insidiously undermines the health of the state, and adds victim to victim until at the end the stage is filled with corpses. It is, as it were, a nihilistic[3] birth in the consciousness of Hamlet that spreads its deadly venom around. That Hamlet is originally blameless, that the King is originally guilty, may well be granted. But, if we refuse to be diverted from a clear vision by questions of praise and blame, responsibility and causality, and watch only the actions and reactions of the persons as they appear, we shall observe a striking reversal of the usual commentary.

If we are to attain a true interpretation of Shakespeare we must work from a centre of consciousness near that of the creative instinct of the poet. We must think less in terms of causality and more in terms of imaginative impact. Now Claudius is not drawn as wholly evil—far from it. We see the government of Denmark working smoothly. Claudius shows every sign of being an excellent diplomatist and king. He is troubled by young Fortinbras, and dispatches ambassadors to the sick King of Norway demanding that he suppress the raids of his nephew. His speech to the ambassadors bears the stamp of clear and exact thought and an efficient and confident control of affairs:

> . . . and we here dispatch
> You, good Cornelius, and you, Voltimand,
> For bearers of this greeting to old Norway;
> Giving to you no further personal power
> To business with the king, more than the scope
> Of these delated articles allow.
> Farewell, and let your haste commend your duty.   (I.ii.33)

The ambassadors soon return successful. Claudius listens to their reply, receives the King of Norway's letter, and hears that young Fortinbras desires a free pass through Denmark to lead his soldiers against the Poles. Claudius answers:

> It likes us well;
> And at our more consider'd time we'll read,
> Answer, and think upon this business.
> Meantime we thank you for your well-took labour:
> Go to your rest; at night we'll feast together:
> Most welcome home!   (II.ii.80)

---

3. **nihilistic** inclined to death and nothingness

Tact has found an easy settlement where arms and opposition might have wasted the strength of Denmark. Notice his reservation of detailed attention when once he knows the main issues are clear; the courteous yet dignified attitude to his subordinates and the true leader's consideration for their comfort; and the invitation to the feast. The impression given by these speeches is one of quick efficiency—the efficiency of the man who can dispose of business without unnecessary circumstance, and so leaves himself time for enjoying the good things of life: a man kindly, confident, and fond of pleasure.

Throughout the first half of the play Claudius is the typical kindly uncle, besides being a good king. His advice to Hamlet about his exaggerated mourning for his father's death is admirable common sense:

> Fie! 'Tis a fault to Heaven,
> A fault against the dead, a fault to nature,
> To reason most absurd; whose common theme
> Is death of fathers, and who still hath cried,
> From the first corse, till he that died to-day,
> 'This must be so.'
> (I.ii.101)

It is the advice of worldly common sense opposed to the extreme misery of a sensitive nature paralysed by the facts of death and unfaithfulness. This contrast points the relative significance of the King and his court to Hamlet. They are of the world—with their crimes, their follies, their shallownesses, their pomp and glitter; they are of humanity, with all its failings, it is true, but yet of humanity. They assert the importance of human life, they believe in it, in themselves. Whereas Hamlet is inhuman, since he has seen through the tinsel of life and love, he believes in nothing, not even himself, except the memory of a ghost, and his black-robed presence is a reminder to everyone of the fact of death. There is no question but that Hamlet is right. The King's smiles hide murder, his mother's love for her new consort is unfaithfulness to Hamlet's father, Ophelia has deserted Hamlet at the hour of his need. Hamlet's philosophy may be inevitable, blameless, and irrefutable. But it is the negation of life. It is death. Hence Hamlet is a continual fear to Claudius, a reminder of his crime. It is a mistake to consider Claudius as a hardened criminal. When Polonius remarks on the hypocrisy[4] of mankind, he murmurs to himself:

---

4. **hypocrisy** pretense of virtue

> O, 'tis too true!
> How smart a lash that speech doth give my conscience!
> The harlot's cheek, beautied with plastering art,
> Is not more ugly to the thing that helps it
> Than is my deed to my most painted word:
> O heavy burthen! (III.i.49)

Again, Hamlet's play wrenches his soul with remorse—primarily not fear of Hamlet, as one might expect, but a genuine remorse—and gives us that most beautiful prayer of a stricken soul beginning, 'O, my offence is rank, it smells to Heaven' (III. iii. 36):

> . . . What if this cursed hand
> Were thicker than itself with brother's blood,
> Is there not rain enough in the sweet heavens
> To wash it white as snow? Whereto serves mercy
> But to confront the visage of offence?

He fears that his prayer is worthless. He is still trammelled [5] by the enjoyment of the fruits of his crime. 'My fault is past,' he cries. But what does that avail, since he has his own crown and his queen still, the prizes of murder? His dilemma is profound and raises the problem I am pointing in this essay. Claudius, as he appears in the play, is not a criminal. He is—strange as it may seem—a good and gentle king, enmeshed by the chain of causality linking him with his crime. And this chain he might, perhaps, have broken except for Hamlet, and all would have been well. But, granted the presence of Hamlet—which Claudius at first genuinely desired, persuading him not to return to Wittenberg as he wished—and granted the fact of his original crime which cannot now be altered, Claudius can hardly be blamed for his later actions. They are forced on him. As King, he could scarcely be expected to do otherwise. Hamlet is a danger to the state, even apart from his knowledge of Claudius' guilt. He is an inhuman—or superhuman—presence, whose consciousness—somewhat like Dostoievsky's Stavrogin— is centred on death. Like Stavrogin, he is feared by those around him. They are always trying in vain to find out what is wrong with him. They cannot understand him. He is a creature of another world. As King of Denmark he would have been a thousand times more dangerous than Claudius. The end of Claudius' prayer is pathetic:

---

5. **trammelled** entangled, as if in a net

> *What then? What rests?*
> *Try what repentance can: what can it not?*
> *Yet what can it when one can not repent?*
> *O wretched state! O bosom black as death!*
> *O limed soul, that, struggling to be free,*
> *Art more engag'd! Help, angels! make assay!*
> *Bow, stubborn knees; and, heart with strings of steel,*
> *Be soft as sinews of the new-born babe!*
> *All may be well.* (III.iii.64)

Set against this lovely prayer—the fine flower of a human soul in anguish—is the entrance of Hamlet, the late joy of torturing the King's conscience still written on his face, his eye a-glitter with the intoxication of conquest, vengeance in his mind; his purpose altered only by the devilish hope of finding a more damning moment in which to slaughter the King, next hastening to his mother to wring her soul too. Which then, at this moment in the play, is nearer the Kingdom of Heaven? Whose words would be more acceptable of Jesus' God? Which is the embodiment of spiritual good, which of evil? The question of the relative morality of Hamlet and Claudius reflects the ultimate problem of this play.

Other eminently pleasant traits can be found in Claudius. He hears of Hamlet's murder of Polonius:

> *O Gertrude, come away!*
> *The sun no sooner shall the mountains touch,*
> *But we will ship him hence: and this vile deed*
> *We must, with all our majesty and skill,*
> *Both countenance and excuse.* (IV.i.28)

Though a murderer himself, he has a genuine horror of murder. This does not ring hypocritical. He takes the only possible course. Hamlet is a danger:

> *His liberty is full of threats to all.* (IV.i.14)

To hurry him from Denmark is indeed necessary: it is the only way of saving himself, and, incidentally, the best line of action in the interests of the state. During the scene of Ophelia's madness (IV. v.) Claudius shows a true and sensitive concern, exclaiming, 'How do you, pretty lady?' and 'Pretty Ophelia!' and after he has told Horatio to look after her, he speaks in all sincerity to his Queen:

O, this is the poison of deep grief; it springs
All from her father's death. O Gertrude, Gertrude,
When sorrows come, they come not single spies,
But in battalions. First, her father slain:
Next, your son gone; and he most violent author
Of his most just remove . . . (IV.v.76)

He continues the catalogue of ills. The people are dissatisfied, Laertes has returned. The problems are overwhelming. When Laertes enters, Claudius rouses our admiration by his cool reception of him:

What is the cause, Laertes,
That thy rebellion looks so giant-like?
Let him go, Gertrude; do not fear our person:
There's such divinity doth hedge a king,
That treason can but peep to what it would,
Acts little of his will. Tell me, Laertes,
Why thou art thus incensed. Let him go, Gertrude.
Speak, man. (IV.v.120)

When he hears of Hamlet's return he plots treachery with Laertes. Everything considered, one can hardly blame him. He has, it is true, committed a dastardly murder, but in the play he gives us the impression of genuine penitence [6] and a host of good qualities. After the murder of Polonius we certainly feel that both the King and the Queen are sane and doing their level best to restrain the activities of a madman. That is the impression given by the play at this point, as we read. If we think in terms of logic, we remember at once that we must side with Hamlet; and we perhaps remember the continual and sudden emergence of a different Hamlet, a Hamlet loving and noble and sane. But intermittent madness is more dangerous by far than obvious insanity. At the best we only prove that Hamlet's madness is justifiable, a statement which makes nonsense; for Hamlet's behaviour, so utterly out of harmony with his environment of eminently likeable people, in that relation may well be called a kind of madness. Whatever it is, it is extremely dangerous and powerful.

I have concentrated on Claudius' virtues. They are manifest. So are his faults—his original crime, his skill in the less admirable kind of policy, treachery, and intrigue. But I would point clearly that, in the movement of the play, his faults are forced on him, and he is distinguished by creative and wise action, a sense of purpose, benevolence, a faith in himself and those around him, by love of his Queen:

---

6. **penitence** regret for one's sins or faults

> *. . . and for myself—*
> *My virtue or my plague, be it either which—*
> *She's so conjunctive to my life and soul,*
> *That as the star moves not but in his sphere,*
> *I could not but by her.* (IV.vii.12)

In short he is very human. Now these are the very qualities Hamlet lacks. Hamlet is inhuman. He has seen through humanity. And this inhuman cynicism, however justifiable in this case on the plane of causality and individual responsibility, is a deadly and venomous thing. Instinctively the creatures of earth, Laertes, Polonius, Ophelia, Rosencrantz and Guildenstern, league themselves with Claudius: they are of his kind. They sever themselves from Hamlet. Laertes sternly warns Ophelia against her intimacy with Hamlet, so does Polonius. They are, in fact, all leagued against him, they are puzzled by him or fear him: he has no friend except Horatio, and Horatio, after the Ghost scenes, becomes a queer shadowy character who rarely gets beyond 'E'en so, my lord', 'My lord—', and such-like phrases. The other persons are firmly drawn, in the round, creatures of flesh and blood. But Hamlet is not of flesh and blood, he is a spirit of penetrating intellect and cynicism and misery, without faith in himself or anyone else, murdering his love of Ophelia, on the brink of insanity, taking delight in cruelty, torturing Claudius, wringing his mother's heart, a poison in the midst of the healthy bustle of the court. He is a superman among men. And he is a superman because he has walked and held converse with death, and his consciousness works in terms of death and the negation of cynicism. He has seen the truth, not alone of Denmark, but of humanity, of the universe: and the truth is evil. Thus Hamlet is an element of evil in the state of Denmark. The poison of his mental existence spreads outwards among things of flesh and blood, like acid eating into metal. They are helpless before his very inactivity and fall one after the other, like victims of an infectious disease. They are strong with the strength of health—but the demon of Hamlet's mind is a stronger thing than they. Futilely they try to get him out of their country; anything to get rid of him, he is not safe. But he goes with a cynical smile, and is no sooner gone than he is back again in their midst, meditating in graveyards, at home with death. Not till it has slain all, is the demon that grips Hamlet satisfied. And last it slays Hamlet himself:

> *The spirit that I have seen*
> *May be the Devil . . .* (II.ii.635)

It was.

Tom Stoppard

from
Rosencrantz and Guildenstern Are Dead

*In this excerpt of the comedy by Tom Stoppard,
Rosencrantz and Guildenstern, the doomed minor
characters in* Hamlet, *prepare to entertain and thereby
learn what has been bothering the prince of Denmark.*

But a flourish—enter CLAUDIUS and GERTRUDE, attended.

> **CLAUDIUS:** *Welcome, dear Rosencrantz . . . (he raises a hand at GUIL while
> ROS bows—GUIL bows late and hurriedly) . . . and Guildenstern.*

He raises a hand at ROS while GUIL bows to him—ROS is still straightening up
from his previous bow and halfway up he bows down again. With his head down,
he twists to look at GUIL, who is on the way up.

> Moreover that we did much long to see you,
> The need we have to use you did provoke
> Our hasty sending.

ROS and GUIL still adjusting their clothing for CLAUDIUS'S presence.

> Something have you heard
> Of Hamlet's transformation, so call it,
> Sith nor th'exterior nor the inward man
> Resembles that it was. What it should be,
> More than his father's death, that thus hath put him,

So much from th'understanding of himself,
I cannot dream of. I entreat you both
That, being of so young days brought up with him
And sith so neighboured to his youth and haviour
That you vouchsafe your rest here in our court
Some little time, so by your companies
To draw him on to pleasures, and to gather
So much as from occasion you may glean,
Whether aught to us unknown afflicts him thus,
That opened, lies within our remedy.

GERTRUDE: Good (*fractional suspense*) gentlemen . . .

They both bow.

He hath much talked of you,
And sure I am, two men there is not living
To whom he more adheres. If it will please you
To show us so much gentry and goodwill
As to expand your time with us awhile
For the supply and profit of our hope,
Your visitation shall receive such thanks
As fits a king's remembrance.

ROS: Both your majesties
Might, by the sovereign power you have of us,
Put your dread pleasures more into command
Than to entreaty.

GUIL: But we both obey,
And here give up ourselves in the full bent
To lay our service freely at your feet,
To be commanded.

CLAUDIUS: Thanks, Rosencrantz (*turning to* ROS *who is caught
unprepared, while* GUIL *bows*) and gentle Guildenstern (*turning to*
GUIL *who is bent double*).

GERTRUDE (*correcting*): Thanks Guildenstern (*turning to* ROS, *who
bows as* GUIL *checks upward movement to bow too—both bent double,
squinting at each other*) . . . and gentle Rosencrantz (*turning to* GUIL,
*both straightening up—*GUIL *checks again and bows again*).

And I beseech you instantly to visit
My too much changed son. Go, some of you,
And bring these gentlemen where Hamlet is.

Two ATTENDANTS *exit backwards, indicating that* ROS *and* GUIL *should follow.*

GUIL: Heaven make our presence and our practices
Pleasant and helpful to him.

GERTRUDE: Ay, amen!

ROS *and* GUIL *move towards a downstage wing. Before they get there,* POLONIUS *enters. They stop and bow to him. He nods and hurries upstage to* CLAUDIUS. *They turn to look at him.*

POLONIUS: The ambassadors from Norway, my good lord, are joyfully
returned.

CLAUDIUS: Thou still hast been the father of good news.

POLONIUS: Have I, my lord? Assure you, my good liege,
I hold my duty as I hold my soul,
Both to my God and to my gracious King;
And I do think, or else this brain of mine
Hunts not the trail of policy so sure
As it hath used to do, that I have found
The very cause of Hamlet's lunacy. . . .

Exeunt—leaving ROS *and* GUIL.

ROS: I want to go home.

GUIL: Don't let them confuse you.

ROS: I'm out of my step here——

GUIL: We'll soon be home and high—dry and home—I'll——

ROS: It's all over my *depth*——

GUIL: —I'll hie you home and——

ROS: —out of my head——

GUIL: —dry you high and——

ROS (*cracking, high*): —over my step over my head body!—I tell you it's all stopping to a death, it's boding to a depth, stepping to a head, it's all heading to a dead stop——

GUIL (*the nursemaid*): There! . . . and we'll soon be home and dry . . . and *high* and dry. . . . (*Rapidly.*) Has it ever happened to you that all of a sudden and for no reason at all you haven't the faintest idea how to spell the word—"wife"—or "house"—because when you write it down you just can't remember ever having seen those letters in that order before . . . ?

ROS: I remember——

GUIL: Yes?

ROS: I remember when there were no questions.

GUIL: There were always questions. To exchange one set for another is no great matter.

ROS: Answers, yes. There were answers to everything.

GUIL: You've forgotten.

ROS (*flaring*): I haven't forgotten—how I used to remember my own name—and yours, oh *yes!* There were answers everywhere you *looked*. There was no question about it—people knew who I was and if they didn't they asked and I told them.

GUIL: You did, the trouble is, each of them is . . . plausible, without being instinctive. All your life you live so close to truth, it becomes a permanent blur in the corner of your eye, and when something nudges it into outline it is like being ambushed by a grotesque.[1] A man standing in his saddle in the half-lit half-alive dawn banged on the shutters and called two names. He was just a hat and a cloak levitating in the grey plume of his own breath, but when he called we came. That much is certain—we came.

ROS: Well I can tell you I'm sick to death of it. I don't care one way or another, so why don't you make up your mind.

GUIL: We can't afford anything quite so arbitrary. Nor did we come all this way for a christening. All *that*—preceded us. But we are comparatively fortunate; we might have been left to sift the whole field of human nomenclature,[2] like two blind men looting a bazaar for their own portraits. . . . At least we are presented with alternatives.

---

1. **grotesque** a fantastic monster made up of various human and animal parts, as in the decorative art of the same name

2. **nomenclature** system of names

ROS: Well as from now——

GUIL: —But not choice.

ROS: You made me look ridiculous in there.

GUIL: I looked just as ridiculous as you did.

ROS (*an anguished cry*): Consistency is all I ask!

GUIL (*low, wry rhetoric*): Give us this day our daily mask.

ROS (*a dying fall*): I want to go home. (*Moves.*) Which way did we come in? I've lost my sense of direction.

GUIL: The only beginning is birth and the only end is death—if you can't count on that, what can you count on?

They connect again.

ROS: We don't owe anything to anyone.

GUIL: We've been caught up. Your smallest action sets off another somewhere else, and is set off by it. Keep an eye open, an ear cocked. Tread warily, follow instructions. We'll be all right.

ROS: For how long?

GUIL: Till events have played themselves out. There's a logic at work—it's all done for you, don't worry. Enjoy it. Relax. To be taken in hand and led, like being a child again, even without innocence, a child—it's like being given a prize, an extra slice of childhood when you least expect it, as a prize for being good, or compensation for never having had one. . . . Do I contradict myself?

ROS: I can't remember. . . . What have we got to go on?

GUIL: We have been briefed. Hamlet's transformation. What do you recollect?

ROS: Well, he's changed, hasn't he? The exterior and inward man fails to resemble——

GUIL: Draw him on to pleasures—glean what afflicts him.

ROS: Something more than his father's death——

GUIL: He's always talking about us—there aren't two people living whom he dotes on more than us.

ROS: We cheer him up—find out what's the matter——

GUIL: Exactly, it's a matter of asking the right questions and giving away as little as we can. It's a game.

ROS: And then we can go?

GUIL: And receive such thanks as fits a king's remembrance.

ROS: I like the sound of that. What do you think he means by remembrance?

GUIL: He doesn't forget his friends.

ROS: Would you care to estimate?

GUIL: Difficult to say, really—some kings tend to be amnesiac, others I suppose—the opposite, whatever that is. . . .

ROS: Yes—but——

GUIL: Elephantine . . . ?

ROS: Not how long—how much?

GUIL: *Retentive*—he's a very retentive king, a royal retainer. . . .

ROS: What are you playing at?

GUIL: Words, words. They're all we have to go on.

Pause.

ROS: Shouldn't we be doing something—constructive?

GUIL: What did you have in mind? . . . A short, blunt human pyramid . . . ?

ROS: We could go.

GUIL: Where?

ROS: After him.

GUIL: Why? They've got us placed now—if we start moving around, we'll all be chasing each other all night.

Hiatus.

ROS (*at footlights*): How very intriguing! (*Turns.*) I feel like a spectator—an appalling business. The only thing that makes it bearable is the irrational belief that somebody interesting will come on in a minute. . . .

GUIL: See anyone?

ROS: No. You?

GUIL: No. (*At footlights.*) What a fine persecution—to be kept intrigued without ever quite being enlightened. . . . (*Pause.*) We've had no practice.

ROS: We could play at questions.

GUIL: What good would that do?

ROS: Practice!

GUIL: Statement! One—love.

ROS: Cheating!

GUIL: How?

ROS: I hadn't started yet.

GUIL: Statement. Two—love.

ROS: Are you counting that?

GUIL: What?

ROS: Are you counting that?

GUIL: Foul! No repetitions. Three—love. First game to . . .

ROS: I'm not going to play if you're going to be like that.

GUIL: Whose serve?

ROS: Hah?

GUIL: Foul! No grunts. Love—one.

ROS: Whose go?

GUIL: Why?

ROS: Why not?

GUIL: What for?

ROS: Foul! No synonyms! One—all.

GUIL: What in God's name is going on?

ROS: Foul! No rhetoric. Two—one.

GUIL: What does it all add up to?

ROS: Can't you guess?

GUIL: Were you addressing me?

ROS: Is there anyone else?

GUIL: Who?

ROS: How would I know?

GUIL: Why do you ask?

ROS: Are you serious?

GUIL: Was that rhetoric?

ROS: No.

GUIL: Statement! Two—all. Game point.

ROS: What's the matter with you today?

GUIL: When?

ROS: What?

GUIL: Are you deaf?

ROS: Am I dead?

GUIL: Yes or no?

ROS: Is there a choice?

GUIL: Is there a God?

ROS: Foul! No *non sequiturs*, three—two, one game all.

GUIL (*seriously*): What's your name?

ROS: What's yours?

GUIL: I asked you first.

ROS: Statement. One—love.

GUIL: What's your name when you're at home?

ROS: What's yours?

GUIL: When I'm at home?

ROS: Is it different at home?

GUIL: What home?

ROS: Haven't you got one?

GUIL: Why do you ask?

ROS: What are you driving at?

GUIL (*with emphasis*): What's your name?!

ROS: Repetition. Two—love. Match point to me.

GUIL (*seizing him violently*): WHO DO YOU THINK YOU ARE?

ROS: Rhetoric! Game and match! (*Pause.*) Where's it going to end?

GUIL: That's the question.

ROS: It's *all* questions.

GUIL: Do you think it matters?

ROS: Doesn't it matter to you?

GUIL: Why should it matter?

ROS: What does it matter why?

GUIL (*teasing gently*): Doesn't it *matter* why it matters?

ROS (*rounding on him*): What's the *matter* with you?

Pause.

GUIL: It doesn't matter.

ROS (*voice in the wilderness*): . . . What's the game?

GUIL: What are the rules?

Enter HAMLET *behind, crossing the stage, reading a book—as he is about to disappear* GUIL *notices him.*

GUIL (*sharply*): Rosencrantz!

ROS (*jumps*): What!

HAMLET *goes. Triumph dawns on them, they smile.*

GUIL: There! How was that?

ROS: Clever!

GUIL: Natural?

ROS: Instinctive.

GUIL: Got it in your head?

ROS: I take my hat off to you.

GUIL: Shake hands.

They do.

ROS: Now I'll try you—Guil—!

GUIL: —Not yet—catch me unawares.

ROS: Right.

They separate. Pause. Aside to GUIL.

Ready?
GUIL (*explodes*): Don't be stupid.
ROS: Sorry.

Pause.

GUIL (*snaps*): Guildenstern!
ROS (*jumps*): What?

He is immediately crestfallen, GUIL *is disgusted.*

GUIL: Consistency is all I ask!
ROS (*quietly*): Immortality is all I seek. . . .
GUIL (*dying fall*): Give us this day our daily week. . . .

Beat.

ROS: Who was that?
GUIL: Didn't you know him?
ROS: He didn't know me.
GUIL: He didn't see you.
ROS: I didn't see him.
GUIL: We shall see. I *hardly* knew him, he's changed.
ROS: You could see that?
GUIL: Transformed.
ROS: How do you know?
GUIL: Inside and out.
ROS: I see.
GUIL: He's not himself.
ROS: He's changed.

GUIL: I could see that.

Beat.

Glean what afflicts him.

ROS: Me?

GUIL: Him.

ROS: How?

GUIL: Question and answer. Old ways are the best ways.

ROS: He's afflicted.

GUIL: You question, I'll answer.

ROS: He's not himself, you know.

GUIL: I'm him, you see.

Beat.

ROS: Who am I then?

GUIL: You're yourself.

ROS: And he's you?

GUIL: Not a bit of it.

ROS: Are you afflicted?

GUIL: That's the idea. Are you ready?

ROS: Let's go back a bit.

GUIL: I'm afflicted.

ROS: I see.

GUIL: Glean what afflicts me.

ROS: Right.

GUIL: Question and answer.

ROS: How should I begin?

GUIL: Address me.

ROS: My dear Guildenstern!

GUIL (*quietly*): You've forgotten—haven't you?

ROS: My dear Rosencrantz!

GUIL (*great control*): I don't think you quite understand. What we are attempting is a hypothesis in which *I* answer for *him*, while *you* ask me questions.

ROS: Ah! Ready?

GUIL: You know what to do?

ROS: What?

GUIL: Are you stupid?

ROS: Pardon?

GUIL: Are you deaf?

ROS: Did you speak?

GUIL (*admonishing*): Not now——

ROS: Statement.

GUIL (*shouts*): Not now! (*Pause.*) If I had doubts, or rather hopes, they are dispelled. What could we possibly have in common except our situation? (*They separate and sit.*) Perhaps he'll come back this way.

ROS: Should we go?

GUIL: Why?

Pause.

ROS (*starts up. Snaps fingers*): Oh! You mean—you pretend to be *him*, and I ask you questions!

GUIL (*dry*): Very good.

ROS: You had me confused.

GUIL: I could see I had.

ROS: How should I begin?

GUIL: Address me.

They stand facing each other, posing.

ROS: My honoured Lord!

GUIL: My dear Rosencrantz!

Pause.

ROS: Am I pretending to be you, then?

GUIL: Certainly not. If you like. Shall we continue?

ROS: Question and answer.

GUIL: Right.

ROS: Right. My honoured lord!

GUIL: My dear fellow!

ROS: How are you?

GUIL: Afflicted!

ROS: Really? In what way?

GUIL: Transformed.

ROS: Inside or out?

GUIL: Both.

ROS: I see. (*Pause.*) Not much new there.

GUIL: Go into details. *Delve.* Probe the background, establish the situation.

ROS: So—so your uncle is the king of Denmark?!

GUIL: And my father before him.

ROS: His father before him?

GUIL: No, my father before him.

ROS: But surely——

GUIL: You might well ask.

ROS: Let me get it straight. Your father was king. You were his only son. Your father dies. You are of age. Your uncle becomes king.

GUIL: Yes.

ROS: Unorthodox.

GUIL: Undid me.

ROS: Undeniable. Where were you?

GUIL: In Germany.

ROS: Usurpation,[3] then.

---

3. **usurpation** illegal seizure of royal power

The Elizabethan Approach

Martin Holmes

Critic Martin Holmes says that Shakespeare wrote his words to be heard, not read. He urges readers to step away from their books and take a front row seat in a theater to fully appreciate Shakespeare's intentions. In the following reading, Prince Charles's version of Hamlet's soliloquy, Prince Charles uses Hamlet's famous soliloquy to point out how clichés and slang have invaded the English language.

THE LONDON CITIZENS who first enjoyed Shakespeare's plays did so in the theatre, and in the theatre alone. Over the space of 15 years, 14 plays were published more or less unofficially as individual quarto[1] texts, some of them very bad ones, but it was not until 1623, when he had been seven years dead, that his collected plays (except for *Pericles, Prince of Tyre*) were available in one volume, the famous First Folio, with a preface advising the reader to 'Read him, therefore, and again, and again, and if then you do not like him, surely you are in some manifest danger not to understand him.' The advice is still good, but we may well be apt to forget that in its day it was not only good but revolutionary. No such work had been published before—a volume of 36 plays, some of them 30 years old, and all, or almost all, of them belonging to an outmoded fashion gently ridiculed by the up-and-coming dramatists of the reign of King James. Yet published it was, and published in the firm conviction that there would be a public for it. Playgoers might wish to revive memories of a piece that had stirred them in the theatre by reading it—and possibly re-reading in some places and skipping in others—in the contemplative quiet of the study, and to increase their

---

1. **quarto** book made up of pages made by folding one sheet of paper into four parts

knowledge and enjoyment of the author by finding what other plays he had written, that they themselves had not had the chance to see performed.

That, after all, is very much our attitude today. We base our knowledge of the plays upon our study of the printed texts rather than our impressions of their effect in performance, and there is a real danger that we may concentrate over-much on the subtleties, real or imagined, of the author's deeper meaning and find ourselves, in his first editors' phrase, in some manifest danger not to understand him. We have reasonable opportunities of seeing a certain number of best-known plays, but not so much a chance of seeing the whole 37, and it is natural that from our youth up we should think of Shakspeare's work as something to be read rather than watched or listened to. There is much enjoyment to be found that way, and unquestionably we gain much from the study of the lines and the slow, measured relish of the poetry, and the philosophy behind it. At the same time, there is something that we miss, and something that deserves better than to be ignored.

Briefly speaking, it is one simple thing—the author's intention. Shakespeare wrote his lines to be spoken in a theatre, to an audience that had come to be entertained, and he could not afford to dwell too long, or to let the audience dwell too long, on points that called for serious contemplation. The great soliloquies, for instance, are not only poetry, they are drama, the unfolding of the processes of a man's or woman's mind, and at the end of any one of them we are that much further on in our understanding of the speaker than we were at the beginning. Words, lines and phrases have to create an immediate impression at the moment of hearing, whether or not that impression lasts in the hearer's mind as the scene goes on. There is no time for going back and pondering, the word or phrase must have its immediate effect, since another is fast upon its heels and will not wait the hearer's leisure. Nowadays we can refresh our memories, or repeat our sensations, by studying the text upon the printed page, but Shakespeare's original audiences could not do anything of the sort, and he had no reason to suppose, when he wrote, that they would ever want to. He had to make his effects at first hearing, or not at all.

The more clearly we keep the thought of the theatre in our minds, the more variety and interest do we find as we read the plays. It is no longer Shakespeare who is speaking, but Hamlet or Rosalind or Falstaff, and they are all different. Let us forget for a moment that sublime figure of the Immortal Swan, who infused something of his own splendour into every character he created, and look instead at the pop-eyed, bald-headed little man whose genius could turn out kings, lovers, villains and ordinary vulgar persons who were all intensely and triumphantly themselves and owed nothing to each other nor even, noticeably, to the individual whose imagination had produced them all. It is this variety that is so important. In printed texts the words 'They fight' or 'Enter a Messenger' occur again and again, because there are not many other words in which one can say so, and we are not encouraged to differentiate one fight, or one messenger, from another. As soon as we see them in performance, however, we see how very different they can be, not only in their natures but in their relation to the story and their effect upon it. They have stopped being 'just Shakespeare' and are part of history or romance instead.

Looking at the plays in this way, as devised to interest, entertain and satisfy a paying public, we find it possible to do more than imagine ourselves as members of an Elizabethan or Jacobean[2] audience. With a very little knowledge of stage conditions, ancient or modern, and of the ordinary tastes of an ordinary playgoer, we can see the plays from not only the spectator's point of view but from the actor's into the bargain. It is all very well to read a long speech, or a brisk passage of dialogue, and admire the poetry, the tenderness or the wit, but it is still more illuminating to consider such a passage occasionally from the transmitting rather than the receiving end. The speech takes on a different quality at once. Instead of being a piece of Shakespeare to be respected, it becomes the expression of somebody's feelings—the character's, primarily, not the author's—and its object is to convey information, or to arouse an emotion of some sort, or possibly both at once. One finds oneself considering afresh what the words actually *mean*, what impression they are intended to convey, and how best one can convey that impression in the process of delivering them. In other words, the passage is coming to life.

Sometimes it fails to do so, and the reader turns from actor to producer. When Hamlet has quarrelled with Laertes at the edge of Ophelia's grave, he suddenly and very naturally tries to make amends, with the words:

> What is the reason that you use me thus?
> I loved you ever, but it is no matter.

What is one to make—what is Hamlet to make—of that second line? Is it all of a piece, and, as A. C. Bradley claimed for it in his *Shakespearean Tragedy*, an expression of the return of 'the old weary misery' in which nothing matters any more? Or is there a change of intention in the middle of the line—is Laertes dismissing the courtesy and brusquely turning away, so that Hamlet abandons his attempt with a word of apology? That is a point for the producer to decide, and the reader, in considering it, may find himself looking at the passage with a producer's eye, and ultimately making his own decision.

This is just as it should be. We have got to the stage of considering the practical problems of interpreting the plays as written, and the next step, if

---

2. **Jacobean** of or relating to James I of England who ruled during the early seventeenth century

we care to take it, leads us to conjectures even more intriguing. We have looked into the meaning of the dialogue that Shakespeare has written, and the likeliest ways of making that dialogue effective on the stage, but now comes the fascinating, tantalizing question in each play—*why did he choose to do it like that?* How much of the form is accepted stage-custom, and how much his own individual variation? Where did he vary it, and is it possible to guess why?

Take, for instance, those little conversational scenes between two or three characters only, and minor characters at that, which are to be found throughout the plays and which are often omitted in performance, to the detriment of the play. They have a reason for being there, and on examination it is not too difficult to find. In a modern (but not a *too* modern) theatre there are moments when tension has been brought to its height, sustained for a while and then mercifully relaxed, whereupon the curtain comes down, the house-lights go up, and the audience can relax likewise. Shakespeare could not count on such variations of lighting or stage-picture, but he could count on variations of mood and verbal cadence, and he was masterly in the use of them. Again and again we see him getting the same effect by following a scene of high tension with a short one that puts no particular strain on the ears or the intellect, because of his consciousness that the audience needs a rest. In *Macbeth,* for example, the murder of Duncan, and the discovery of that murder by the horrified household, are immediately followed by a short, quiet scene between Ross and an old man, with one or two shrewd comments by Macduff, and in the succeeding act the emotional tension of the banquet scene, which reduces Lady Macbeth herself to a state of nervous exhaustion, gives way to a rhyming passage for Hecate and the Witches (despised by the literary, but unexpectedly effective on the stage) and a conversation between Lennox and an unnamed Lord, reflecting on the state of affairs in general, and particularly on the circumstances of Macbeth's rise to power.

When we have occasion to consider the succession of incidents that make up a scene, and of scenes that make up an act, we find that they are no longer forming a mere chain of events, like the summarizing of a plot. They are seen, instead, to be forming a *pattern.* We begin to understand what the author is intending by his arrangement of successive scenes of emotion, narrative or contemplation, and by increasing that understanding we are increasing our own interest and enjoyment. We have been let in, as it were, behind the scenes, and can possibly catch a glimpse—occasional only, but fascinating when it comes—of Shakespeare's mind at work. The playwright appears to us as that rare combination of master-poet and practical man of the theatre, and the things he is doing take on for us an added interest, and an added value, because we are beginning to have an idea why he does them. It may not be an accurate idea, but it has at least set us on the way to considering the Literary Figure as having been at the same time a human being, obliged in the course of his work to tackle certain practical, human problems, and that itself is much.

To Be or Not to Be

H. R. H. Charles, Prince of Wales

"Well, frankly, the problem as I see it
At this moment in time is whether I
Should just lie down under all this hassle
And let them walk all over me,
5   Or, whether I should just say, 'OK,
I get the message,' and do myself in.
I mean, let's face it, I'm in a no win
Situation, and quite honestly,
I'm so stuffed up to here with the whole
10 Stupid mess that, I can tell you, I've just
Got a good mind to take the quick way out.
That's the bottom line. The only problem is:
What happens if I find out that when I've bumped
Myself off, there's some kind of a, you know,
15 All that mystical stuff about when you die,
You might find you're still—know what I mean?"

(the original soliloquy)

To be, or not to be—that is the question:
Whether 'tis nobler in the mind to suffer
The slings and arrows of outrageous fortune
Or to take arms against a sea of troubles,
5   And by opposing end them. To die—to sleep—
No more; and by a sleep to say we end
The heartache, and the thousand natural shocks
That flesh is heir to. 'Tis a consummation
Devoutly to be wish'd. To die—to sleep.
10   To sleep—perchance to dream: ay, there's the rub!
For in that sleep of death what dreams may come
When we have shuffled off this mortal coil,
Must give us pause. There's the respect
That makes calamity of so long life.
15   For who would bear the whips and scorns of time,
Th' oppressor's wrong, the proud man's contumely,
The pangs of despis'd love, the law's delay,
The insolence of office, and the spurns
That patient merit of th' unworthy takes,
20   When he himself might his quietus make
With a bare bodkin? Who would these fardels bear,
To grunt and sweat under a weary life.
But that the dread of something after death—
The undiscover'd country, from whose bourn
25   No traveller returns—puzzles the will,
And makes us rather bear those ills we have
Than fly to others that we know not of?
Thus conscience does make cowards of us all,
And thus the native hue of resolution
30   Is sicklied o'er with the pale cast of thought,
And enterprises of great pith and moment
With this regard their currents turn awry
And lose the name of action.

<table>
</table>

| Carolyn Heilbrun | # The Character of Hamlet's Mother |

Author Carolyn Heilbrun urges readers of Shakespeare to take a closer look at the character of Gertrude. Heilbrun contends there is more to Gertrude's character than meets the eye.

THE CHARACTER OF HAMLET'S MOTHER has not received the specific critical attention it deserves. Moreover, the traditional account of her personality as rendered by the critics will not stand up under close scrutiny of Shakespeare's play.

None of the critics of course has failed to see Gertrude as vital to the action of the play; not only is she the mother of the hero, the widow of the Ghost, and the wife of the current King of Denmark, but the fact of her hasty and, to the Elizabethans, incestuous marriage, the whole question of her "falling off," occupies a position of barely secondary importance in the mind of her son, and of the Ghost. Indeed, Freud and Jones see her, the object of Hamlet's Oedipus complex,[1] as central to the motivation of the play.[a] But the critics, with no exception that I have been able to find, have accepted Hamlet's word "frailty" as applying to her whole personality, and have seen in her not one weakness, or passion in the Elizabethan sense, but a character of which weakness and lack of depth and vigorous intelligence are the entire explanation. Of her can it truly be said that carrying the "stamp of one defect," she did "in the general censure take corruption from that particular fault."

The critics are agreed that Gertrude was not a party to the late King's murder and indeed knew nothing of it, a point which on the clear evidence

---

1. **Oedipus complex** unconscious sexual attraction of a son toward his mother, whereas the son sees his father as a rival

of the play, is indisputable. They have also discussed whether or not Gertrude, guilty of more than an "o'er-hasty marriage," had committed adultery with Claudius before her husband's death. I will return to this point later on. Beyond discussing these two points, those critics who have dealt specifically with the Queen have traditionally seen her as well-meaning but shallow and feminine, in the pejorative[2] sense of the word: incapable of any sustained rational process, superficial and flighty. It is this tradition which a closer reading of the play will show to be erroneous.

Professor Bradley describes the traditional Gertrude thus:

> The Queen was not a bad-hearted woman, not at all the woman to think little of murder. But she had a soft animal nature and was very dull and very shallow. She loved to be happy, like a sheep in the sun, and to do her justice, it pleased her to see others happy, like more sheep in the sun. . . . It was pleasant to sit upon her throne and see smiling faces around her, and foolish and unkind in Hamlet to persist in grieving for his father instead of marrying Ophelia and making everything comfortable. . . . The belief at the bottom of her heart was that the world is a place constructed simply that people may be happy in it in a good-humored sensual fashion.[b]

Later on, Bradley says of her that when affliction comes to her "the good in her nature struggles to the surface through the heavy mass of sloth."

Granville-Barker is not quite so extreme. Shakespeare, he says,

> gives us in Gertrude the woman who does not mature, who clings to her youth and all that belongs to it, whose charm will not change but at last fade and wither; a pretty creature, as we see her, desperately refusing to grow old. . . . She is drawn for us with unemphatic strokes, and she has but a passive part in the play's action. She moves throughout in Claudius' shadow; he holds her as he won her, by the witchcraft of his wit.[c]

Elsewhere Granville-Barker says "Gertrude who will certainly never see forty-five again, might better be 'old.' [That is, portrayed by an older, mature actress.] But that would make her relations with Claudius—and *their* likelihood is vital to the play—quite incredible." Granville-Barker is saying here that a woman about forty-five years of age cannot feel any sexual passion or arouse it. This is one of the mistakes which lie at the heart of the misunderstanding about Gertrude.

---

2. **pejorative** belittling

Professor Dover Wilson sees Gertrude as more forceful than either of these two critics will admit, but even he finds the Ghost's unwillingness to shock her with knowledge of his murder to be one of the basic motivations of the play, and he says of her "Gertrude is always hoping for the best."[d]

Now whether Claudius won Gertrude before or after her husband's death, it was certainly not, as Granville-Barker implies, with "the witch-craft of his wit" alone. Granville-Barker would have us believe that Claudius won her simply by the force of his persuasive tongue. "It is plain," he writes, that the Queen "does little except echo his [Claudius'] wishes; sometimes—as in the welcome to Rosencrantz and Guildenstern—she repeats his very words," though Wilson must admit later that Gertrude does not tell Claudius everything. Without dwelling here on the psychology of the Ghost, or the greater burden borne by the Elizabethan words "witchcraft" and "wit," we can plainly see, for the Ghost tells us, how Claudius won the Queen: the Ghost considers his brother to be garbage, and "lust," the Ghost says, "will sate itself in a celestial bed and prey on garbage." "Lust"—in a woman of forty-five or more—is the key word here. Bradley, Granville-Barker, and to a lesser extent Professor Dover Wilson, misunderstand Gertrude largely because they are unable to see lust, the desire for sexual relations, as the passion, in the Elizabethan sense of the word, the flaw, the weakness which drives Gertrude to an incestuous marriage, appalls her son, and keeps him from the throne. Unable to explain her marriage to Claudius as the act of any but a weak-minded vacillating woman, they fail to see Gertrude for the strong-minded, intelligent, succinct, and, apart from this passion, sensible woman that she is.

To understand Gertrude properly, it is only necessary to examine the lines Shakespeare has chosen for her to say. She is, except for her description of Ophelia's death, concise and pithy in speech, with a talent for seeing the essence of every situation presented before her eyes. If she is not profound, she is certainly never silly. We first hear her asking Hamlet to stop wearing black, to stop walking about with his eyes downcast, and to realize that death is an inevitable part of life. She is, in short, asking him not to give way to the passion of grief, a passion of whose force and dangers the Elizabethans were aware, as Miss Campbell has shown.[e] Claudius echoes her with a well-reasoned argument against grief which was, in its philosophy if not in its language, a piece of commonplace Elizabethan lore. After Claudius' speech, Gertrude asks Hamlet to remain in Denmark, where he is rightly loved. Her speeches have been short, however warm and loving, and conciseness of statement is not the mark of a dull and shallow woman.

We next hear her, as Queen and gracious hostess, welcoming Rosencrantz and Guildenstern to the court, hoping, with the King, that they may cheer Hamlet and discover what is depressing him. Claudius then tells Gertrude, when they are alone, that Polonius believes he knows what is upsetting Hamlet. The Queen answers:

> I doubt it is no other than the main,
> His father's death and our o'er-hasty marriage.

This statement is concise, remarkably to the point, and not a little courageous. It is not the statement of a dull, slothful woman who can only echo her husband's words. Next, Polonius enters with his most unbrief apotheosis[3] to brevity. The Queen interrupts him with five words: "More matter, with less art." It would be difficult to find a phrase more applicable to Polonius. When this gentleman, in no way deterred from his loquacity,[4] after purveying the startling news that he has a daughter, begins to read a letter, the Queen asks pointedly "Came this from Hamlet to her?"

We see Gertrude next in Act 3, asking Rosencrantz and Guildenstern, with her usual directness, if Hamlet received them well, and if they were able to tempt him to any pastime. But before leaving the room, she stops for a word of kindness to Ophelia. It is a humane gesture, for she is unwilling to leave Ophelia, the unhappy tool of the King and Polonius, without some kindly and intelligent appreciation of her help:

> And for your part, Ophelia, I do wish
> That your good beauties be the happy cause
> Of Hamlet's wildness. So shall I hope your virtues
> Will bring him to his wonted way again,
> To both your honors.

It is difficult to see in this speech, as Bradley apparently does, the gushing shallow wish of a sentimental woman that class distinctions shall not stand in the way of true love.

At the play, the Queen asks Hamlet to sit near her. She is clearly trying to make him feel he has a place in the court of Denmark. She does not speak again until Hamlet asks her how she likes the play. "The lady doth protest too much, methinks" is her immortal comment on the player queen. The scene gives her four more words: when Claudius leaps to his feet, she asks "How fares my Lord?"

I will for the moment pass over the scene in the Queen's closet, to follow her quickly through the remainder of the play. After the closet scene, the

---

3. **apotheosis** highest development of something
4. **loquacity** talkativeness

Queen comes to speak to Claudius. She tells him, as Hamlet has asked her to, that he, Hamlet, is mad, and has killed Polonius. She adds, however, that he now weeps for what he has done. She does not wish Claudius to know what she now knows, how wild and fearsome Hamlet has become. Later, she does not wish to see Ophelia, but hearing how distracted she is, consents. When Laertes bursts in ready to attack Claudius, she immediately steps between Claudius and Laertes to protect the King, and tells Laertes it is not Claudius who has killed his father. Laertes will of course soon learn this, but it is Gertrude who manages to tell him before he can do any meaningless damage. She leaves Laertes and the King together, and then returns to tell Laertes that his sister is drowned. She gives her news directly, realizing that suspense will increase the pain of it, but this is the one time in the play when her usual pointed conciseness would be the mark neither of intelligence nor kindness, and so, gently, and at some length, she tells Laertes of his sister's death, giving him time to recover from the shock of grief, and to absorb the meaning of her words. At Ophelia's funeral the Queen scatters flowers over the grave:

> Sweets to the sweet! Farewell!!
> I hoped thou shouldst have been my Hamlet's wife.
> I thought thy bride-bed to have decked, sweet maid,
> And not have strewed thy grave.

She is the only one present decently mourning the death of someone young, and not heated in the fire of some personal passion.

At the match between Hamlet and Laertes, the Queen believes that Hamlet is out of training, but glad to see him at some sport, she gives him her handkerchief to wipe his brow, and drinks to his success. The drink is poisoned and she dies. But before she dies she does not waste time on vituperation;[5] she warns Hamlet that the drink is poisoned to prevent his drinking it. They are her last words. Those critics who have thought her stupid admire her death; they call it uncharacteristic.

In Act 3, when Hamlet goes to his mother in her closet his nerves are pitched at the very height of tension; he is on the edge of hysteria. The possibility of murdering his mother has in fact entered his mind, and he has just met and refused an opportunity to kill Claudius. His mother, meanwhile, waiting for him, has told Polonius not to fear for her, but she knows when she sees Hamlet that he may be violently mad. Hamlet quips with her, insulting her, tells her he wishes she were not his mother, and when she, still retaining dignity, attempts to end the interview, Hamlet seizes her

---

5. **vituperation** abusive language

and she cries for help. The important thing to note is that the Queen's cry "Thou wilt not murder me?" is not foolish. She has seen from Hamlet's demeanor that he is capable of murder, as indeed in the next instant he proves himself to be.

We next learn from the Queen's startled "As kill a King?" that she has no knowledge of the murder, though of course this is only confirmation here of what we already know. Then the Queen asks Hamlet why he is so hysterical:

> What have I done, that thou dar'st wag thy tongue
> In noise so rude against me?

Hamlet tells her: it is her lust, the need of sexual passion, which has driven her from the arms and memory of her husband to the incomparably cruder charms of his brother. He cries out that she has not even the excuse of youth for her lust:

> O shame where is thy blush? Rebellious hell,
> If thou canst mutine in a matron's bones,
> To flaming youth let virtue be as wax
> And melt in her own fire. Proclaim no shame
> When the compulsive ardor gives the charge,
> Since frost itself as actively doth burn,
> And reason panders will.

This is not only a lust, but a lust which throws out of joint all the structure of human morality and relationships. And the Queen admits it. If there is one quality that has characterized, and will characterize, every speech of Gertrude's in the play, it is the ability to see reality clearly, and to express it. This talent is not lost when turned upon herself:

> O Hamlet, speak no more!
> Thou turn'st mine eyes into my very soul,
> And there I see such black and grained spots
> As will not leave their tinct.

She knows that lust has driven her, that this is her sin, and she admits it. Not that she wishes to linger in the contemplation of her sin. "No more," she cries, "no more." And then the Ghost appears to Hamlet. The Queen thinks him mad again—as well she might—but she promises Hamlet that she will not betray him—and she does not.

Where, in all that we have seen of Gertrude, is there the picture of "a soft animal nature, very dull and very shallow"? She may indeed be "animal" in the sense of "lustful." But it does not follow that because she wishes to continue a life of sexual experience, her brain is soft or her wit unperceptive.

Some critics, having accepted Gertrude as a weak and vacillating woman, see no reason to suppose that she did not fall victim to Claudius' charms before the death of her husband and commit adultery with him. These critics, Professor Bradley among them, claim that the elder Hamlet clearly tells his son that Gertrude has committed adultery with Claudius in the speech beginning "Ay that incestuous, that adulterate beast." Professor Dover Wilson presents the argument:

> Is the Ghost speaking here of the o'er-hasty marriage of Claudius and Gertrude? Assuredly not. His "certain term" is drawing rapidly to an end, and he is already beginning to "scent the morning air." Hamlet knew of the marriage, and his whole soul was filled with nausea at the thought of the speedy hasting to "incestuous sheets." Why then should the Ghost waste precious moments in telling Hamlet what he was fully cognisant of before? . . . Moreover, though the word "incestuous" was applicable to the marriage, the rest of the passage is entirely inapplicable to it. Expressions like "witchcraft," "traitorous gifts," "seduce," "shameful lust," and "seeming virtuous" may be noted in passing. But the rest of the quotation leaves no doubt upon the matter. . . .

Professor Dover Wilson and other critics have accepted the Ghost's word "adulterate" in its modern meaning. The Elizabethan word "adultery," however, was not restricted to its modern meaning, but was used to define any sexual relationship which could be called unchaste, including of course an incestuous one.[f] Certainly the elder Hamlet considered the marriage of Claudius and Gertrude to be unchaste and unseemly, and while his use of the word "adulterate" indicates his very strong feelings about the marriage, it would not to an Elizabethan audience necessarily mean that he believed Gertrude to have been false to him before his death. It is important to notice, too, that the Ghost does not apply the term "adulterate" to Gertrude, and he may well have considered the term a just description of Claudius' entire sexual life.

But even if the Ghost used the word "adulterate" in full awareness of its modern restricted meaning, it is not necessary to assume on the basis of this single speech (and it is the only shadow of evidence we have for such a conclusion) that Gertrude was unfaithful to him while he lived. It is quite probable that the elder Hamlet still considered himself married to Gertrude, and he is moreover revolted that her lust for him ("why she would hang on him as if increase of appetite had grown by what it fed on") should have so easily transferred itself to another. This is why he uses the expressions "seduce," "shameful lust," and others. Professor Dover Wilson has himself said "Hamlet knew of the marriage, and his whole soul was filled with nausea at the thought of the speedy hasting to incestuous sheets"; the soul of the elder Hamlet was undoubtedly filled with nausea too, and this could well explain his using such strong language, as well as his taking the time to mention the matter at all. It is not necessary to consider Gertrude an adulteress to account for the speech of the Ghost.

Gertrude's lust was, of course, more important to the plot than we may at first perceive. Charlton Lewis, among others, has shown how Shakespeare kept many of the facts of the plots from which he borrowed without maintaining the structures which explained them. In the original Belleforest story, Gertrude (substituting Shakespeare's more familiar names) was daughter of the king; to become king, it was necessary to marry her. The elder Hamlet, in marrying Gertrude, ousted Claudius from the throne.[g] Shakespeare retained the shell of this in his play. When she no longer has a husband, the form of election would be followed to declare the next king, in this case undoubtedly her son Hamlet. By marrying Gertrude, Claudius "Popp'd in between th' election and my hopes," that is, kept young Hamlet from the throne. Gertrude's flaw of lust made Claudius's ambition possible, for without taking advantage of the Queen's desire still to be married, he could not have been king.

But Gertrude, if she is lustful, is also intelligent, penetrating, and gifted, with a remarkable talent for concise and pithy speech. In all the play, the person whose language hers most closely resembles is Horatio. "Sweets to the sweet," she has said at Ophelia's grave. "Good night sweet prince," Horatio says at the end. They are neither of them dull, or shallow, or slothful, though one of them is passion's slave.

a. Shakespeare, William: *Hamlet*, with a psycho-analytical study by Ernest Jones, M.D. London: Vision Press, 1947, pp. 7–42.

b. Bradley, A. C., *Shakespearean Tragedy* (New York: Macmillan, 1949), p. 167.

c. Granville-Barker, Harley, *Prefaces to Shakespeare* (Princeton University Press, 1946), I, 227.

d. Wilson, J. Dover, *What Happens in Hamlet* (Cambridge University Press, 1951), p. 125.

e. Campbell, Lily B. *Shakespeare's Tragic Heroes* (New York: Barnes & Noble, 1952), pp. 112–113.

f. See Joseph, Bertram, *Conscience and the King* (London: Chatto and Windus, 1953), pp. 16–19.

g. Lewis, Charlton M., *The Genesis of Hamlet* (New York: Henry Holt & Co., 1907), p. 36.